ADVANCE PRAISE FOR MINDFUL MD

"There is an epidemic of physician burnout. Dr. Gazelle's book, *Mindful MD*, gives us a thoughtful and supportive path not only toward healing but also wellbeing."
—James R. Doty, MD, *New York Times* bestselling author of *Into the Magic Shop: A Neurosurgeon's Quest to Discover the Mysteries of the Brain and the Secrets of the Heart*

"Physician burnout is of concern to all of us. Dr. Gazelle weaves together real-life stories of physicians and reveals the power mindfulness has to help them thrive."
—Tara Brach, author of *Radical Acceptance* and *Trusting the Gold*

"In *Mindful MD*, Dr. Gail Gazelle provides practical tools to combat one of the most serious problems afflicting doctors and healthcare professionals today: burnout. This is essential reading for struggling physicians."
—Sandeep Jauhar, *New York Times* bestselling author of *Doctored: The Disillusionment of an American Physician*

"Dr. Gazelle provides an antidote for the pain physicians feel today. Burnout threatens the health of both patients and physicians. Doctors may not have total control over their environment, but they aren't helpless to exert influence. In this powerful book, Dr. Gazelle explains how mindfulness can provide significant relief and how connectivity with colleagues adds joy. Physicians aren't the source of burnout, but that doesn't mean they shouldn't do what's in their power to make the best of the healthcare opportunities that exist today.

Reading this book is the first step."
—Robert Pearl, MD, former CEO, Kaiser Permanente,
and author of *Uncaring* and the *Washington Post* bestseller,
Mistreated

"This is a particularly timely contribution, especially given
well-documented increases in practitioner burnout and
attrition around the globe. Dr. Gazelle shows not only a deep
understanding of the stressors that physicians face every
day, but further provides accessible strategies for cultivating
mindfulness, an approach that bolsters autonomy and self-
determination, and realistic discussions of how to bring more
awareness, meaning, and vitality into one's practice and life."
—Richard Ryan, PhD, author of *Self-Determination Theory*

"Incredible! Dr. Gazelle helps us see the power mindfulness has
to restore autonomy and humanity in healthcare."
—Marshall Goldsmith, PhD, *New York Times* bestselling author
of *The Earned Life, Triggers,* and *What Got You Here Won't Get You
There*

"As a physician herself, Dr. Gazelle candidly explains what
makes doctors vulnerable to burnout. Then she prescribes the
medicine—mindfulness and self-compassion practices that
doctors can apply on the spot to enhance well-being, even when
the system is stacked against them. To everyone in healthcare:
You can do this!"
—Christopher Germer, PhD, author of *The Mindful Path to Self-
Compassion*

"Physician burnout is real, very painful and costly, for the
physicians but also for the patients who deserve engaged and
thriving health care providers. Dr. Gazelle's wonderful book
opens the door to helping doctors to help themselves and to
re-connect with the passion that got them into medicine in the

first place."
—Christiane Wolfe, MD, author of *A Clinician's Guide to Teaching Mindfulness*

"Physician burnout is a major epidemic. Kudos to Dr. Gazelle for showing us a way to regain joy and meaning."
—Sanjiv Chopra, MD, Harvard Medical School, and author, with Deepak Chopra, of *Brotherhood*

"We physicians need to move from martyrdom to mindfulness as a way to save ourselves and change our systems. We can start right now by reading this book."
—Judson Brewer, MD, PhD, *New York Times* bestselling author of *Unwinding Anxiety* and *The Craving Mind*

"Dr. Gazelle's vast work at the intersection of healthcare and contemplative practice is presented in this book with the perfect balance of background science and practical tips for incorporating these transformative practices into our daily lives. This book is a gift to all physicians and true care givers, especially those facing the day to day challenges of modern healthcare. It should be required reading for all medical trainees and practitioners."
—Jonathan Fisher, MD, Co-Founder and Chair, Ending Clinician Burnout Global Community and Summits

"This is a much-needed book by a physician who is an experienced coach for doctors who are suffering from burnout. As Dr. Gazelle accurately points out, "we can hand our happiness over to a broken healthcare system or we can take it back into our own hands." She gives many real-life examples of how mindfulness and meditation give us the ability to notice and re-program our habitual, unhelpful ways of thinking and reacting, and points out that neuroscience shows that this reprogramming actually rewires the circuits in our brain.

These changes take practice, but they are the best medicine for helping us find ease and contentment in our lives at work and at home. They are a way for us to continue our most vital work in a healthcare system that is at best extremely challenging and at worst, fatally flawed."
—Jan Chozen Bays, MD, Zen teacher, and author of *Mindful Medicine: 40 Simple Practices to Help Healthcare Professionals Heal Burnout and Reconnect to Purpose*

"This book is a must read! While acknowledging the systemic factors of our healthcare system that contribute significantly to burnout, Dr. Gazelle provides us a path forward to reclaim joy and fulfillment that is within our control. Rather than provide Band-Aid solutions, she gets to the root cause of suffering— our mind. Using simple but powerful mindfulness techniques interwoven with stories of her clients, Dr. Gazelle shows us how to gain understanding and mastery of our minds. Physicians, students, and other healthcare providers along with their families will benefit greatly from this book!"
—Sanj Katyal, MD, author of Amazon #1 bestseller *Positive Philosophy: Ancient and Modern Wisdom to Create a Flourishing Life*

Mindful MD

6 WAYS MINDFULNESS RESTORES YOUR AUTONOMY AND CURES HEALTHCARE BURNOUT

BY GAIL GAZELLE, MD
WITH DAAVI GAZELLE

Cover by Sheila Parr
Editing by Daavi Gazelle

Title: Mindful MD. 6 Ways Mindfulness Restores Your Autonomy and Cures Healthcare Burnout
First edition, June 2023
ISBN: 978-0-9798176-4-9 (ebook) | 978-0-9798176-0-1 (paperback) | 978-0-9798176-2-5 (hardcover)
Library of Congress Control Number: 2023909098
Created and printed in the United States of America

Learn more about Dr. Gail Gazelle at www.GailGazelle.com

Special discounts may be available on quantity book purchases. Contact info@gailgazelle.com for information.

Also by Gail Gazelle, MD

Everyday Resilience. A Practical Guide to Build Inner Strength and Weather Life's Challenges (2020)

The Daily Dose of Calm free mini-mindfulness course (2020)

Harvard Heath Guide. Mindfulness Support for Alzheimer's Caregivers (2013)

~

By Daavi Gazelle

The Kids Who Get In. A New Authentic Approach to College Admissions (2020)

This book is dedicated to all healthcare professionals, who show up and give their best each and every day in the service of caring for those in need. It is also dedicated to the hundreds of physicians who have entrusted me as their coach. Their courage and resilience is an inspiration and model for what is possible for caregivers and the entire field of healthcare to thrive.

CONTENTS

INTRODUCTION

When Rosemary reached out to me that icy, cold January morning, I could hear that she was on the edge.

"I can't keep going like this," she told me, her voice choking up. "I'm completely overwhelmed. All my autonomy has been taken away, and if I don't spend hours every evening catching up on labs and charts, they'll dock my pay. It's all miserable and I'm not accomplishing anything anyway. I spend all day at work stressed, I come home stressed, and I wake up stressed—it feels like the stress never ends.

"Between charting late into the night, haggling with insurance companies to authorize tests when I should be with my patients, and listening to administrators constantly telling me how to run my practice, I no longer enjoy my work. I've never been as smart as others anyway. They know how to manage all this stress and they're better doctors than me to boot! Maybe I've never really had what it takes."

Rosemary, and the hundreds of other physicians who have called me when things have boiled over, had lost her sense of purpose and motivation as a physician. She felt powerless in her practice and was in a state of burnout.

To Rosemary, it seemed like everyone but her was able to cope with these difficulties, that others were clearly better doctors, and even that she was some sort of imposter. Despite being a beloved and respected internist, Rosemary felt like she didn't measure up. She was exhausted and had lost sight of the good she was doing; all of her energy was focused on what was not going well. She was pondering leaving the practice of medicine entirely.

Rosemary, like half of American physicians (and those of many other nations), was burned out. The numbers are staggering in almost every specialty: Physicians are struggling mightily.[1-4] Physicians suffer from depression and anxiety at twice the rates of the general population,[5-8] and tragically, 300–400 US physicians die at their own hands every year—the equivalent of two medical school classes.[9-12] The impact extends beyond physicians—every aspect of impaired physician well-being contributes to erosion of empathy, medical error, and disruption of morale for the entire healthcare team.[13-20]

The impact of burnout is profound—for you, the physician, for the system, and for all of us who need care.

The pressures and busyness the modern physician experiences are plentiful and real; there has never been a more difficult time to be a physician. With the growing corporatization of the field, healthcare has become like most sectors of the economy: Focused on productivity and profits. Physicians see unrealistic numbers of patients in a day, spend hours typing into the electronic medical record (EMR), and care for patients in often understaffed, stressful, and dysfunctional environments.

We (read: you) have our pay tied to perverse financial incentives and find our days filled with multiple below-grade tasks. We spend hours outside of work trying to keep up with the electronic record and an ever-full inbox. We are expected to fix the myriad of social problems that plague our patients while social workers and case managers are laid off. Our days are full of emotionally taxing moments, given all the tragedy we see. Being a physician is more than a full-time job, and, of course, we also have to attend to the demands of life outside of work—parenting, marriage, caring for aging parents, managing one's own health and finances, and more.

The COVID-19 pandemic only compounded these struggles. We witnessed colleagues falling ill after not receiving appropriate protective equipment, faced cuts in income due to the halting of elective procedures and furloughs, and all but homeschooled our kids in addition to caring for our patients. Many of us experienced the trauma of being unable to fulfill our commitment to save lives as our world became polarized around masks, vaccines, and science. While dramatic headlines have slowed, the lingering impact on the healthcare system and its stalwarts (us) remains.

On top of these day-to-day burdens, what drives the nail into the coffin are the massive expectations placed on us, by society and by ourselves. Our training teaches us to be perfect, to always have the answers, to be the invulnerable captain of the team, to get it all "right." Nearly every one of the hundreds of physicians I have coached struggles with perfectionism and harsh self-criticism, and these and other damaging mental patterns lead to that energy-draining feeling of inadequacy and despair Rosemary was feeling when she called me. On a camel's back of long hours, emotionally taxing work, endless electronic records, and the stresses of life beyond work, this sense of not measuring up is often the straw that sends it all tumbling down.

While there is no doubt that the busyness and pressure we physicians experience is incredibly stressful, on top of this is *the busyness and pressure* created and amplified by our own minds. We've invested hundreds of thousands of dollars and nearly a decade in our medical training, and now that we don the white coat, our careers are nothing like we thought they'd be. In addition to the rampant dysfunction around us, our inner worlds are chaotic; all the busyness and pressure can make everything feel like it's falling apart.

While there is little we can do about that rampant dysfunction, **fortunately, we have control over our inner worlds**—and that's where mindfulness comes in.

For those of you having trouble getting through each day, I promise that there is a way out of this struggle: A way into a balanced life of meaning, fulfillment, happiness, and true autonomy both within and outside your practice.

I've seen this happen with countless physicians, but before I saw it with any of them, I saw it with myself.

Let me share my story.

I had a messy childhood, to put it mildly. I grew up in a household that looked like a normal, happy American family on the outside: My mom was a seamstress, my dad was a college professor, and my sister and I were happy-appearing kids. We baked Toll House cookies after school and watched *The Brady Bunch* before bed.

But beneath this veneer there was a lot of abuse, and I went through most of my childhood filled with pain and fear. There was a great deal that I couldn't control, but I *could* control my grades, and I learned early on to make sure they were always perfect. Academics and achievement became my escape, so throughout my adolescence, I studied, and studied, and studied. I studied my way to an Ivy League college, and into and through medical school.

I aspired to work in end-of-life care because my childhood experience fostered a deep sense of isolation, motivating me to help alleviate the suffering and isolation experienced by people forced to face the final chapter of their lives.

In medical school, however, I struggled. It wasn't so much the long hours as the constant expectation to always have the right answer, the incessant comparisons to peers, being pimped and shamed on rounds, and the lack of space for the emotions that arose along the way.

As I moved into practice, I felt like an imposter, caught up in comparing myself to colleagues I assumed were smarter and more accomplished than me. The perfectionism that had served me well in becoming a doctor was a huge thorn in my side once I was one. I beat myself up constantly for the smallest missteps. My brow was deeply furrowed—people often see pictures of me from then (over 20 years ago) and comment on how much older I looked!

Along the way, I decided to have a child, even though I was single. Raising my son, Daavi, has been the most rewarding experience of my life.

But my feelings of imposter-hood and inadequacy didn't stop at the end of the workday. When I was at work, I felt guilty for not being with my son. *I'm selfish to spend so much time on my career. Other parents are better at this than me.* When I was with my son, I couldn't turn off worries about my patients, along with a nagging sense that I should be doing more. *What if I've missed something? Other doctors are better at this than me.* Then I'd beat myself up for not being able to turn off my mind and be more present. *What's wrong with me that my mind won't ever quiet down so I can actually relax and just be?*

When things continued to worsen, I turned to the only strategies I knew—those that had helped me thus far: Head down, nose to the grindstone, strive for perfection, and just make it to the next big goalpost.

Needless to say, these strategies didn't work. They simply drove me deeper into burnout. I wasn't sleeping, I suffered from chronic tension headaches and jaw pain, and one day I was so overwrought that when I tripped on one of Daavi's Legos, I lashed out at him. That's when I realized that something had to give. I had already changed jobs, gotten different administrators, and switched EMRs, all of which simply equated to rearranging the deck chairs on my rapidly sinking ship.

Getting past burnout meant that I had to try something new, and that meant looking inside myself.

I spent time unpacking my childhood trauma—wounds that I had spent decades repressing with work and achievement. I learned how to take care of myself. I realized just how much of my energy was being drained by beating myself up and comparing what I knew within myself to the polished exteriors of those around me. And I realized that no matter how hard I tried, I would never achieve perfection.

I also began to see that feeling like a victim of my work was keeping me as just that. As odd as it may sound, it had never previously occurred to me that I could choose how I related to my circumstances. I couldn't change the fact that the EMR was taking up more and more of my day. I couldn't change the way nurses, administrators, or patients acted. I couldn't change the fact that practicing medicine and being a parent isn't an easy combination.

I could only change the way I responded to all of this.

The way I talked to myself, how I took care of myself, and how I showed up at work and at home every day—these were things I could change. Changes that were rooted in being aware of how I was mentally multiplying my struggles at work and at home, without even realizing it.

As I saw how much of my anguish came from my own mind, I channeled all the hard work and studiousness that got me through each day as a student into learning everything I could about stress, burnout, healing, and the workings of the human mind.

And I stumbled into mindfulness.

Far from being someone who had trekked to monasteries in Nepal or spent their teenage years chanting on a meditation cushion—and with my skeptical academic mind—I initially thought that mindfulness was a lot of fluff and woo-woo.

But I rapidly saw how the mental mastery that mindfulness afforded helped me manage the difficulties I faced, and just how much my own mind had kept me mired in burnout and misery for far too long. I tried out bits and pieces of what I learned and went back to the drawing board again and again.

Eventually, though, there was no denying it—this mindfulness stuff was working. I was happier, calmer, and more productive, and everyone could see it. Patients and friends alike commented, "You look so much happier. Are you in love?" My house was calmer and I had more time with my son; we started a nightly ritual of cooking dinner and watching *Shark Tank*.

Of course, work was still challenging, but now I had the tools I needed to shift it from being overwhelming to being manageable. After throwing the kitchen sink at burnout, mindfulness was the only thing that was working. So, I dove in headfirst.

Besides meditating, taking courses, and attending numerous weeklong silent retreats, I went on to complete a 2-year training as a mindfulness teacher. In that capacity, I now teach mindfulness and resilience at Harvard Medical School and across the globe.

Additionally, in my 20 years of caring for thousands of terminally ill patients and their loved ones, I learned a great deal about mindfulness and resilience. I saw many die hooked up to machines in an intensive care unit, trapped in a state of denial, emotional pain, and anguish, never having closure with those they held most dear. I also saw just as many move from anger and denial to a place of acceptance, forgiveness, and peace. By observing how patients faced the end of their lives, I learned about the fundamental autonomy available even in our most difficult times: Our ability to decide how we respond to the difficulties we face.

With the rise in levels of physician burnout, I wanted to help colleagues cope, so I pivoted from hospice work and became a physician coach. Helping physicians overcome burnout has become my life's work.

Over the past decade, I have coached more than 500 physicians all over North America—and I've seen how working intentionally with their minds (read: mindfulness) has helped them make massive leaps in well-being, happiness, and effectiveness.

Of course, mindfulness isn't a magic penicillin for burnout. And it's no omission of the system's large role in physician burnout. But accounting for what **we can control**, overcoming imposter syndrome, overwhelm, stress, fatigue, and frustration is only possible where the rubber meets the road—in our own mental and emotional responses.

I have seen the power mindfulness has to help physicians be more agile in handling the stresses of the profession and in bringing greater presence and compassion not just to their patients, but to themselves as well. I have seen how mindfulness has helped them (just like those facing their illness—or even death) shift from frustration, anger, and despair to a rightful sense of autonomy and fulfillment. This was the case for Rosemary, as well as for many others.

Now, let's get back to you and your story (particularly if you're one of the many physicians struggling with burnout). Reading this introduction, you might be thinking this is going to be yet another book claiming that meditating, doing yoga, and keeping a gratitude journal are going to erase the dysfunction in today's healthcare system.

So let me be clear: This book is not going to rejig the health-care system, recenter our hospitals on compassion and respect for clinicians, or fix the multiple deficiencies that COVID-19 has compounded. The unfortunate truth is that there is an over-whelming amount that is broken that you and I aren't going to fix anytime soon. But in the midst of a broken system, you can live a life of fulfillment, balance, and presence.

This starts by focusing on what you *can* control.

You only have one life to live, and although you may not be responsible for the circumstances you face in healthcare, you are the one who decides how you cope with them.

The good news is that there is a way out of this suffering and burnout, a path of empowerment and choice—a return to loving, present relationships, happiness, purpose, and fulfillment, both at work and at home.

It starts with us as individuals. There is no other way. To sit around and wait for the system to change just leaves you handing your happiness and career satisfaction over to a broken, bureau-cratic mess. With the mindfulness tools you'll learn from this book, you can regain peace of mind and career fulfillment today.

It won't be easy, and it will require a massive dose of personal responsibility, willingness to change, commitment, patience, and mindfulness.

This book will give you the tools to tackle the challenges of a problematic healthcare system head-on. The tools to regain con-trol, happiness, compassion, and fulfillment within your practice and at home. The tools to reconnect with why you became a physician in the first place. And the tools to help you see why the perfectionism, self-criticism, and problem-focused mindset that have gotten you this far may now be a good part of what is making you miserable.

You'll learn:

- The mental patterns instilled as early as elementary school that set future physicians up for burnout
- How medical training creates hyper–self-critical physicians, and how to turn this inner critic off
- Everything medical school didn't teach you about managing your most important instrument—your mind
- How to work with your busy mind and turn it off when the workday is over
- How to protect your energy stores in the context of a dysfunctional system
- How to manage your patterns of emotional reactivity
- How to be compassionate toward yourself
- The massive ripple effect that comes from overcoming burnout
- How to transcend burnout in an "upward spiral"

In short: **How to be mindful**.

Mindfulness is about stepping out of mental stories and filters that too often obscure our view. It is about questioning our thoughts and assumptions, our beliefs, and our fixed ways of viewing ourselves and others. It is about disengaging the automatic pilot that many of us inadvertently live in and stepping into fully conscious and "aware" living. It is about shedding a lens that defines happiness by what happens to us and realizing that whatever misfortunes and difficulties occur, we always have a choice in how we respond to them.

We'll begin our journey with the roots of these dysfunctional patterns—our training and, before that, our childhoods. We'll see how the "fixed medical mindset" (a hyper-focus on problems and a habit of "diagnosing" our way through life) derails us and how the expectations that the white coat brings all too often lead to our suffering. We'll learn about the habits we carry that may have been necessary to *become* doctors but completely derail us once we *are* doctors.

We'll examine what it takes to get past burnout and become a *Mindful MD*, a physician with a fully balanced, purposeful, integrated life and career. You will see what your life and work can be when you utilize mindfulness to step out of the judgments, stories, beliefs, and assumptions that have ensnared you for too long.

Along the way, I'll share stories of dozens of real-life physicians, arguably the central actors in the healthcare ecosystem. After each chapter, you'll have a chance to begin practicing what you learn and get answers to questions that may arise. We'll look at what mindfulness can do not just for us as individuals, but what the ripple effects are on our friends, families, colleagues, and patients. You will see how each of the 6 ways supports your autonomy and cures burnout independently and, as you read further, in concert with one another.

You don't have to be a physician to benefit from this book. Nurses, technicians, therapists, administrators, executives, and all others working in healthcare will find invaluable tools in these pages. If you are someone who is concerned about physician well-being, a patient, and if you are not in healthcare at all, I know that you will find many things you can relate to. You'll learn tools to work with your own busy mind so that you, too, can reap the benefits of a mindful approach to your work and life.

You are beginning your most important journey yet—a journey to balance, fulfillment, and the life and career you deserve.

Let's dive in.

Note: This book contains real-life stories of physicians and others. To protect anonymity, the author has taken the liberty of altering names and minor details that do not change the true nature of the person, their words, and their circumstances.

PART I

"If you put people up on pedestals, there's only one way for them to go and that is down."
—Samantha Bond

T he average day in the physician's work life is not designed to prevent burnout and may even appear designed to cause burnout. Additionally, however, and below the surface, there are roots formed early on that put physicians on a path of worry, fear, and anxiety, as well as difficulty coping with the uncertainty and unpredictability of the modern healthcare landscape. These hidden forces, combined with highly stressful work environments, lack of autonomy over work conditions, and overly abundant demands, create the perfect breeding ground for burnout.

In Part I, we examine those forces—mental patterns fostered through years of training and beginning as early as childhood. We'll see how being identified as special and gifted from a young age, being trained to focus on problems and diagnose, and being harshly criticized for any failure or misstep, creates perfection-istic, self-critical, burned-out doctors.

We'll introduce mindfulness and begin to see the ways these problematic roots can be regrown.

The Roots of Burnout

*"Students undergo a conversion in the third year of medical school
—not pre-clinical to clinical, but pre-cynical to cynical."*
—Abraham Verghese

Despite busy days with double-booking and complicated patients, Raphaela, a 49-year-old infectious disease specialist, often found her mind wandering to an event from her internship, more than 20 years prior. It was early in the year, a time of intense learning, when interns depend on their resident to come to their rescue if needed.

Raphaela and her resident were caring for a Vietnam veteran with prostate cancer that had metastasized to bone. The patient had been admitted a week earlier with severe back and leg pain that was unusually difficult to control. The pain was so intense that the patient lay curled up in a ball, withdrawn from everything around him.

They consulted the pain team and instituted multiple trials of medication. But the pain persisted. Raphaela pored over journal articles and looked for anything that hadn't been tried. She read about an obscure approach and pitched it to the team, who gave it a try. And it worked. Finally, the patient's pain was under control. The attending and resident praised Raphaela for her commitment and for the good work she had done—her discovery had saved the day.

But this wasn't the event that Raphaela revisited. Now, years later, Raphaela rarely thinks back to this positive experience. Instead, her mind frequently returns to what felt like a catastrophic failure.

She had received an urgent call from a panic-stricken nurse who had mistakenly given the patient an extra dose of morphine and was afraid that the patient would have an opioid-induced respiratory arrest. Raphaela paged her resident but didn't get an answer. Racing up to the patient's room, she ordered the nurse to administer a dose of Narcan to reverse the morphine's effects.

The medication so effectively reversed the morphine that the patient began convulsing in pain. The resident rushed into the room and shouted at Raphaela: "How could you have given him Narcan? You should have known he would be okay!"

Even though the patient wound up being fine, over 2 decades later, Raphaela still replays that scene. It was horrifying enough that her error had contributed to the patient's pain; what stood out for Raphaela, however, were the resident's accusatory words, which still rang in her ears today. For the rest of her internship, this resident often harped on her lapse, while her positive input was quickly forgotten.

Like the one B– on a report card full of As, Raphaela couldn't help but focus on what she had done wrong. She rarely reminded herself of all the ways she contributed to patient care (or, for that matter, anything else she did well).

Quietly, insidiously, and unseen to Raphaela (like many other physicians), the roots of burnout were being laid down. Way below the surface of what appeared to be a successful and fulfilling career, the roots were growing, spreading, and forming the foundation for many difficulties ahead.

For many physicians, these roots begin forming well before we even enter our medical training. Let's examine how perfectionism and an implicit fear of making mistakes can be fostered at a young age, stemming from a seemingly innocuous place: Being labeled as special.

Special From an Early Age

Individuals who go into the practice of medicine bring a host of wonderful qualities: Compassion, intelligence, discipline, critical thinking, love of learning, creativity, resilience, a passion for excellence, and a deep sense of purpose. We join the profession prepared to make major sacrifices in the service of helping fellow human beings live their best and fullest lives.

At the same time, because of their high intellectual and academic prowess, physicians learn early on that they are somehow different from others—or, simply put, *special*. Although being special may sound like something to strive for, it often becomes a source of difficulty as we progress in our careers.

Let's consider Dan, who was labeled early on as "the smart one." The third child in a rural Midwestern American farming family, he was, as his parents could see, noticeably different from his two siblings. While they were roughhousing in the barn and eager to be involved in 4-H agriculture projects, Dan could be found nestled in a corner reading a book. His contributions to the farm were limited to those that scratched his nerdy itch: Developing blueprints for new cattle pens, identifying the most effective fertilizer ratios, and assessing livestock weight to dairy output ratios. Even though he lost in every sport the neighborhood kids played, he was unbeatable at Scrabble.

Although Dan was often picked on by the other boys, he could always take refuge in the smile of the teacher as he correctly solved yet another math, spelling, or science problem. He always had the answer to whatever questions the teacher posed, and loved going to school; it was the place where he excelled, the place where he received validation, the place where accolades were plentiful. School was the place where Dan shined and where his identity as special formed.

Regardless of whether their childhood was full of hay bales and early-morning farm chores, and whether they fit the nerd archetype as well as Dan, many physicians can recall a similar sense of standing out due to their academic aptitude. As a result of the pattern of being academically gifted and earning good grades, the future physician is often defined by one narrow aspect of who they are. They begin to sense that their worth and identity lie in the validation provided by top grades, the teacher's approval, and always having the right answer.

A feedback loop begins where the young whiz kid is motivated by appearing smart and earning external affirmation, as opposed to an internal compass of success. This begins a pattern of dependence on those around us to affirm our worth and specialness, even from the strangers we sit next to on planes (as we'll see in a bit).

Special Creates Problems

Being special, with accolades aplenty, has obvious upsides. Having a positive self-identity is a crucial ingredient to achievement, and, outside of the extreme of narcissism, thinking highly of one's own abilities in a vacuum is rarely a bad thing. The problem with special, however, is that it is based on comparisons to those around you.

After all, special means that you're in a different club than others. In that club, there are limited spots available, so there's competition to secure whatever defines your specialness. Top grades. Prestigious training. Awards and academic standing.

Because there are a limited number of spots in the special club, you have to hold tight to your specialness as there's only so much of it to go around. Instead of a healthy sense of abundance and collegiality, there's a sense of scarcity, starting with the competitive process of getting in. From early on, this sets up a calculus whereby I can't be happy about your success because it could detract from mine.

This came up for Julia, a mid-career geriatrician, when she was recruiting a new faculty member to her academic division. She knew they needed more staff and was excited to get funding to fill the spot. At the same time, though, she was uncomfortable about who this person would be. "What if they're smarter than me?" she confided in me. "What if they're a star, and I get shown up as the low-bar researcher I am? I want to get somebody good, but I'm also scared about it, and I feel like crap for thinking this way."

Then there is Atish, a 48-year-old addiction specialist, who confided that he hated it when other physicians won awards or received accolades. "It's like there's an inner voice asking, 'Why are they getting this and not me?' I know I shouldn't be feeling this way, but I do."

We can see how Julia's and Atish's identity as special led to insecurity about being one-upped, disrupting their ability to appreciate the talents and accomplishments of their peers.

Does any of this ring a bell?

Special Breeds Insecurity

Special also puts us into a box that leaves us fearful of exposure. Our identity has been shaped by only one part of ourselves, and we're left vulnerable to the fear that we'll be found out—that people will see that we're really not so special after all. In this way, the seeds of imposter syndrome begin to take root.

David put it this way: "For me, it started in grade school. I was constantly told that I was the brainy one—by my parents, teachers, and other kids. I loved getting all the attention, but I had this sneaking suspicion that maybe it wasn't all true. And the bar kept rising. The more I did well, the more people expected me to do well. I kept up the farce in college, med school, and residency, living in constant fear of being found out. Even when I did well, I knew I could fall off the pedestal at any time.

"In my career as a surgeon, I knew I was competent, but every time I went into the OR, I had this clutching in my gut that this was going to be the time that people would find out the truth. Then there was the time a few years back when a patient had a serious complication and nearly died. I was sure my time had come. But it didn't, and that's when things really started coming off the rails. It's like I'm living with this constant fear because I know it's only a matter of time."

The problem with depending on external recognition is the fear that comes with it. Because we depend on the world seeing our perfect, glossy (special) exteriors, we look at our messy, complicated interiors and fear we'll be found out one day. Similarly, we look around at other people's shiny exteriors and feel inadequate. Sadly, what many of these patterns add up to is a lot of fear. In the words of physician and author Danielle Ofri: "[T]he truth is that fear overwhelms even the most psychologically sound and well-adjusted trainee. At some point it happens to nearly every single person who travels through the medical training process. If you don't believe me, just ask any doctor you know."[1]

Of course, physicians are deserving of a healthy dose of recognition—we sacrifice a great deal, devoting years to developing the skills needed to excel in the care of others. We toil for countless hours, delay gratification, and amass significant debt. After four years of medical school, at least three years of residency, and perhaps multiple years of fellowship and advanced training, we see college friends move to six-figure corporate jobs, get married, buy their first home, and already make a significant dent in their student loans. Enduring a decade plus of highly specialized training and education to become a doctor is certainly a special accomplishment!

That being said, an identity predicated on being special creates a vacuum of affirmation—a hole forever in need of being filled. We can find ourselves seeking external approval to feel valued and whole. When it is not provided—such as when we are employees in corporate entities where non-physicians occupy every rung of leadership—many of us find ourselves adrift. Our identity has formed around standing out and being recognized as special. No longer being seen that way is something I have seen contribute to burnout in many of the physicians I have coached.

Special and the People Around Us

Our sense of specialness can also negatively impact those around us.

Perhaps, as a patient, you've had the experience of sitting in a busy waiting room, with your doctor running late. When they apologize, you likely understand and let it go. If they don't, however, you can feel an uneasy sense that they believe their time is valuable and yours is not. It's not a good feeling, is it?

I've come to see my own relationship with being special, and I'll share an embarrassing anecdote to illustrate. It came to the fore on a JetBlue flight to LA while I was reading a journal article on morphine dosing in kidney failure. The well-dressed and well-coiffed woman in the middle seat looked up from her laptop, and we began chatting about our trips. After some small talk about freezing temperatures in Boston versus sunny warmth in SoCal, I politely asked her what she did for work.

As she replied, I could feel my jaw tighten as I leaned forward in my seat. I strained to put an interested look on my face, but then it struck me: I didn't actually care what she did or even who she was. I realized that I had just asked her the question so I could give my own answer—that I was a physician, that I was important, that I was *special*.

I'm certainly not proud to own this moment, but I share it here since it served to open an important window of mindful awareness. Flying in the face of the humility I prided myself on, I began to see that whether it was chatting with parents at my son's Little League game or meeting someone new, I wasn't really interested in what they did for a living. I was just waiting for an opening to tell them I was a doctor. That I wasn't just Gail, a physician, a mother, and an educator—I was *Doctor* Gazelle.

This realization of how central my identity as special was left me wondering: *Was I an isolated example of a complete narcissist or did other physicians experience the same thing?* Apart from making us poor conversationalists on planes and in the Little League bleachers, did wanting to be recognized as special come hand in hand with feeling superior to (and more important than) others?

Additionally, perhaps this sense of being special makes us less receptive to the views of others. Perhaps it sets us up for dissatisfaction in a healthcare environment where we are no longer at the top.

As Malcolm Gladwell explores in his bestselling book, *David and Goliath*, doctors-to-be like Dan and others can suffer from the "big fish in a small pond" phenomenon. Following a student he names Caroline Sacks, Gladwell shows how this academic exemplar went from being perched at the top of her class for years, her identity forming around her academic smarts, to then losing her footing when others excelled beyond her. Using this example, he sheds light on the phenomenon of the academic achiever whose sense of themselves forms around being intellectually superior to others.

Gladwell writes, "And that feeling—as subjective and ridic-ulous and irrational as it may be—*matters*. How you feel about your abilities—your academic self-concept—in the context of your classroom shapes your willingness to tackle challenges and finish difficult tasks. It's a crucial element in your motivation and confidence."[2]

More than this, it becomes a crucial element in your very sense of who you are in the world—your self-worth. Caroline's and Dan's self-concepts were based on an external valuation of their worth, not the fullness of who they were. And expecting others to view us as special means handing over this self-worth to those we encounter.

When our identity forms around *special,* we become:

- Dependent on external affirmation
- Reluctant to admit weakness or vulnerability
- Fearful and defensive about feedback
- Perfectionistic
- Afraid of being exposed as a fraud

Now, I want to make the important point here that being labeled as special is like being dealt a two and a seven off-suit in poker—it's a bad hand! We physicians are not to be blamed for feeling special; we come by it honestly. As you'll soon see, though, mindfulness helps us move past this toward true inner confidence. Because identification with being special limits us, and from a young age sets us on a path toward burnout. Let's see how this looks when we enter medical school and training.

Earning the White Coat

After being labeled as academically gifted, and special, physicians-to-be are put through the ringer in pursuit of their white coats.

Consider the sheer level of perfection it takes to get into medical school. With an average acceptance rate of less than 6 percent, and as low as 2 percent, it is now nearly impossible to get in. While you may have applied a number of years ago (I definitely did), that doesn't change the fact that the path to becoming a doctor has never been easy—and requires near flawlessness in the classroom and on the MCAT.

We can see this with Omar, a client of mine who, like many physicians, grew up in a family where his grades were the prize of his parents' eyes. His parents had fled Afghanistan, and, like many immigrant (and non-immigrant) parents, their focus was on his academic success. Because of his natural academic aptitude, Omar was considered the golden boy. But he had aspirations beyond academics: He was infatuated with basketball. His Jordan 1 high-tops were his prized possession.

Omar's parents thought that basketball was a waste of his talents—something that would only get in the way of his academic success—and refused to allow him to join the school basketball team. Singularly focused on grades and report cards, his parents frequently compared him to his younger sister.

Omar recalled how before every report card was opened, his parents sat him and his sister down at the dining room table, and, with an aura of suspense, they pulled up their grades on the computer. As a freshman in high school—and having never scored below an A—Omar brought home a report card that included a B−. This time, his sister had gotten nothing lower than an A−. His parents beamed at his sister. Omar received painful silence from his father, who wouldn't even make eye contact with him for the rest of the day. Although his father said no words, his disappointment was palpable. Omar told me that, after the shaming he received from his father, he knew that he was never going to let anything less than an A happen again.

Notice how Omar wasn't praised for how hard he studied, how curious he was, or what great questions he asked. All that mattered were the letters on that screen each quarter, the letters that indicated whether Omar was "smart" or not. While the shaming may have sent Omar back to the books, it was fear that dragged him forward; he was no longer propelled by his former love of learning. Along with being special was immense pressure and conditional praise—conditional on impressive outcomes at the end of each quarter.

In high school, physicians-to-be are encouraged to load up on as many difficult courses as possible, forgoing extracurricular passions that may not look as impressive on a college application. Upon landing a coveted spot in a prestigious undergraduate institution, the game immediately begins again, now in pursuit of medical school admission. Once again, the entire process revolves around perfectionism and appealing to an external marker of success (grades), resulting in an unfortunate dwindling of genuine passion and an overemphasis on pressure, external reward, and fear.

Does any of this sound familiar?

Unfortunately, this dependence on perfection and external validation is only honed during medical training.

So Much to Learn

Those who get into medical school (the most perfectionistic and special of all doctor-hopefuls) are eager: To learn, to be accepted, to be seen for the smart and caring young person they are. To learn how to take care of fellow human beings. To don the white coat and experience the prestige and praise that comes with it.

What happens next?

These eager young adults begin their trajectory of learning: Facts upon facts, disease upon disease, the biochemistry of every pathway in the human body, and the mechanism of action of thousands of medications.

What started as a commitment to compassion and caring quickly becomes an exercise in rote memorization and repetition.

Then there's more to learn. More facts to memorize. More hours studying in solitude in the library. More tests. So much to take in and absorb. So much to be responsible for. Such a high-stakes undertaking, as well as an exciting journey of learning and discovery. Attending your first newborn delivery. Being part of a code team that successfully resuscitates a patient the same age as your father. Watching a brain tumor excision up close.

So many experiences that cement your choice of career.

But the hours are long and expectations are high. There are many challenging situations. Amidst all the powerful learning, character building, bonding, and professional growth, there is also a great deal of pressure.

Sadly, this pressure comes at a cost. Numerous studies reveal a high prevalence of psychological distress among medical students, including depression, anxiety, stress, and burnout.[3-5] Indeed, research reveals that at least half of all US medical students experience some form of psychological distress. For residents, the numbers are just as concerning.[6-8] A recent review of studies that included 4,600 residents in a wide range of specialties found that, overall, 36 percent suffered from burnout.[9]

Nonetheless, many physicians have wonderfully formative experiences during training and look positively on this part of their career journey. And, of course, the system of training has many merits. But it also reinforces and rewards multiple patterns that seed the roots of burnout and distress: Perfectionism, external affirmation, fierce self-criticism, and overwork.

Praised for What?

One wonders: Is all of this simply the price of becoming a physician? Or are there ways that medical training itself contributes to distress, both during training and for years to come? At the same time, what is it that is most valued in the process? Is it learning, growing, and developing? Is it the care of patients? Or is it more about having the right answer and never getting anything wrong?

Most of us would hope that it is the care of patients. In truth, though, many physicians would say that their medical training was more about how they performed on rounds, whether they knew the correct answer or not, how they compared to their peers, and whether they appeared vulnerable or all-knowing, capable, and in charge.

In fact, *being* smart may have been less important than *looking* smart.

Patrick described it this way: "I never felt like I was good enough. I got an okay score on the MCAT but nothing to write home about. And during the first and second years, I found that other students had a way of approaching tests that I just didn't have. There seemed to be some kind of game that I never really understood the rules for. It was being the one who had memorized the lists and could spout off about some esoteric finding or the latest research they just happened to be up on. I never got credit for being the one who actually spent time at the bedside."

Patrick's experience is not unique and correlates with a significant body of data supporting a loss of empathy as students progress through their medical training.[10–12]

In the words of Abraham Verghese, famed Stanford professor and author, "What we need in medical schools is not to teach empathy, as much as to preserve it—the process of learning huge volumes of information about disease, of learning a specialized language, can ironically make one lose sight of the patient one came to serve; empathy can be replaced by cynicism."[13]

The vast amounts of pressure, memorization, and studying that medical students are faced with can ironically move the focus away from what medicine is all about: Taking care of patients. Medical students are praised for many tangible, quantitative things, but they are often overlooked concerning the human side of medicine—for factors such as empathy, kindness, and caring.[14–15]

Ratings, Rankings, and Comparisons, Oh My!

Already primed by our specialness to have our worth predicated upon external metrics, we find ourselves at the mercy of the many ratings, rankings, and comparisons we experience in our training.

While premeds are well acquainted with tests and rankings, the phenomenon of comparisons is one that medical school and residency take to a whole other level. Instead of simply being compared to your peers, now the comparisons span a much greater swath. You are compared to trainees a year ahead of you, to residents, and to attendings. You are compared to your co-residents—to equally brilliant, perfectionistic, special young people who were each the stars of their undergraduate institutions. Before you know it, you can find yourself making these comparisons yourself.

Additionally, family doctors are compared to internists, and internists to cardiologists and other medical specialists. Medical specialists are compared to surgeons, and general surgeons are compared to vascular, oncology, cardiac, and neurosurgeons. Unfortunately, the comparisons invariably focus on deficiency: Pathologists, radiologists, and psychiatrists are derided as not being real doctors, while medical and surgical specialists stand at the top of the pack.

The practice of medicine involves a well-established hierarchy, and the medical student witnesses this every day, which impacts their choice of specialty and fuels insecurity.

This was the case for Amy, someone who entered medical school planning on becoming a pediatrician. The granddaughter of a small-town pediatrician, Amy had grown up witnessing her granddad care for kids in her sister's and brother's classes and had always seen it as her calling as well. But when attending physicians asked what specialty she wanted to go into, Amy saw the look of condescension on their faces when she shared her choice.

"You're smarter than that," was the typical response. "Why waste your talents on pediatrics?" After hearing enough of these comments, Amy abandoned her goal and switched to internal medicine. It wasn't where her heart was, but it was apparent that internal medicine would lead to greater respect from those within the profession.

Sadly, it doesn't take long for the astute student to see that there is a game being played here, a game of winners and losers, and it is one that you can't risk falling short in. As acknowledged by Dr. Robert Pearl, former CEO of Permanente Medical Group, "[T]he healthcare hierarchy remains a powerful force in determining the mental health and overall happiness of physicians."[16]

Theodore Roosevelt once said that "comparison is the thief of joy." Comparisons steal our joy by fostering what we refer to in mindfulness as the *comparing mind*. Giving this tendency a name helps us spot what our minds are up to.

In fact, I often liken mindfulness to making a diagnosis, something physicians are experts at. We look at symptoms, tests, and imaging results, and we discern a pattern. Once we see the pattern (i.e., make the diagnosis), we can intervene, or treat.

In the same way, we can begin to diagnose what our minds are up to. We can examine the phenomenon of *special* and the complexities of our training and see a pattern emerging in terms of how we are set up for difficulty. We can spot when we're getting caught by the comparing (or judging, worrying, fearful) mind. As you will soon see, with this awareness, or diagnosis, we can then work with (read: treat) these patterns with much greater agility.

The Hidden Curriculum

In addition to their status in the hierarchy, medical students learn early on the importance of having the right answer. Ask physicians what they recall from training, and many, like Raphaela, have a story involving the price they paid for getting something wrong.

Medical training tends to be somewhat black-and-white. Students learn that there can be only one right answer, often with little credit given for applying yourself, doing your best, or trying your hardest. Instead, it's all about getting it right.[17-18] Yet, what happens when there is no right answer? When we're living more in the gray than the black-and-white—like when there is a pandemic from a previously unseen lethal virus?

Medical students learn early on that it is their job to always have the answer; this is part of medical school's "hidden curriculum," the implicit transmission of norms and values that contribute to the formation of professional identity, behaviors, and attitudes of the future physician. While parts of this process are positive, shaping young minds into mature professionals, there is no question that much is deleterious.

The hidden curriculum, per the American College of Physicians, "leads to behaviors and qualities that are inconsistent with empathic, ethical, and professional conduct."[19] Included in the hidden curriculum are expectations of invulnerability and stoicism—always the captain of the team, always in command, never revealing signs of personal weakness or asking for help, and always having the correct answer.[20-22]

For example, a male surgeon I coached recalled being labeled "a girl" after admitting that he didn't know the diagnosis of a rare disease. A female cardiologist, who was post-call and had fainted from dehydration on rounds as an intern, was the brunt of incessant jokes by the male attending about her clear weakness and inadequacy as a physician. An accomplished gynecologist, after not knowing the name of a surgical instrument during residency, received a threat from her chief of never being allowed back in the OR.

Another problematic practice, as physicians know all too well, is being "pimped" on rounds. In this common process, a trainee is subjected by an attending or another superior to a series of difficult and often intentionally unanswerable questions, taken to the point where the trainee falters, is no longer able to answer, and is then blamed and shamed for their ignorance. As noted by UCSF educators in a 2021 article, "'Pimping,' a long-held method of reinforcing hierarchy and belittling learners through toxic quizzing, should be eliminated. This practice is the epitome of reducing someone's self-worth on the basis of performance and reinforces the fixed mindset."[23-26]

From where I sit, pimping represents everything wrong with medical training.

Perfect or a Failure

In addition to the emphasis on ratings, rankings, comparisons, and invulnerability, medical students learn that expectations are high and a great deal is required of them. Of course, taking care of fellow humans is a high-stakes enterprise and pursuing excellence is a key aspect of being a physician. But there is a large difference between doing your best and expecting perfection. In fact, the push for perfection becomes problematic in a number of ways.

You've probably heard that perfectionism is the enemy of the good. This is actually a vast understatement. Perfectionism is the enemy of ease, presence, resilience, and well-being.

Ironically enough, perfectionism is what many physicians can thank for much of their success. Getting near-perfect grades and MCAT scores and getting diagnoses "right" are crucial steps for earning a white coat. However, perfectionism also creates a heavy burden and rapidly becomes a maladaptive behavior, characterized by fear of shattering the positive perceptions of others, rumination about decisions and negative outcomes, an excessive need for validation, and overgeneralization of missteps to definitions of one's character and worth.[27–30]

Moreover, perfection is, by definition, an unattainable standard; expecting it sets up the future physician for a sense that they are coming up short. Sadly, the unrealistic standard of perfection leads to rumination about performance, replaying our actions, judging and comparing ourselves, and paying disproportionate attention to ways we are measuring up. Perfectionism begets obsessiveness and limits one's ability to shrug off the inevitable foibles that come with being human.

Third-year medical student Imogen Thompson put it this way: "The quintessential 'good' medical student isn't difficult to picture. Her dedication borders on obsession and pays dividends in the form of excellent marks, supervisor praise, and the knowledge that she is responsible for raising the bar out of reach of the rest. Good medical students usually also count flashcards among their brief list of hobbies, and are those for whom sleep deprivation is a competitive sport. Success in medical school is almost wholly defined by exam results, and there are no bonus marks for being well-rounded."[31]

Perfectionism means that nothing is ever good enough, fueling almost constant dissatisfaction with our work, our relationships, and ourselves. In often subtle ways, our minds establish a guide-post around the ideal of perfection, with everything compared and assessed based on how it measures up. The emphasis is not on doing one's best and being good enough.

To repeat, **perfectionism means that *nothing* is ever good enough.**

Rather than shooting for excellence, something that is attain-able and sustainable, the bar is something we can never reach. We are left in a constant state of striving. Striving to do more, do better, and do it all perfectly. Striving to prove our worth. Striving to avoid being shamed.

All this striving is an exhausting way to live.

Perfectionism also fuels procrastination, a dysfunctional pat-tern of disproportionate attention to detail, berating ourselves for not achieving perfection, believing that this berating will improve performance, anxiety about performance, lack of con-fidence, and an inability to appreciate what we do well. It can be an extreme and debilitating downward cycle, one that later con-tributes to the difficulty many physicians have completing their electronic notes.

Where does a need to be perfect come from? When our identities are rooted in specialness and academic superiority, we rely on maintaining a "perfect" exterior to ensure that others see us in this way. These patterns are hammered home through the rigorous undergraduate and medical school entrance and educational processes that weed out any student less than 100 percent committed to leaping through each and every hoop placed before them. And all too often this commitment stems from perfectionism and the implicit fear that comes with it. While this chicken-and-egg cycle may help in passing exams and earning us our white coats, it can be debilitating once we're actually with patients.

Rashid, a 32-year-old surgery resident who came to coaching after taking a 3-month leave from his position, put it this way: "Med school made me OCD and anxious. I don't know how I made it through. But when I got into my residency, that's when things fell apart. My mind was caught in rumination and fear of making mistakes. I thought that continuously ruminating and analyzing any mistake was the only way to improve. Then things began to feel kind of do-or-die; there was nothing enjoyable. If I wasn't doing things perfectly, I would sort of flip out. When I presented a case on rounds, I worried so much about how every word sounded that I'd lose myself and almost begin speaking gibberish. It was all becoming disorganized and chaotic. That's when it all unraveled and I had no choice but to leave."

Needless to say, trying to maintain this image of perfection is exhausting and contributes to the burnout experienced by medical students. As one medical student put it, "Perfectionism leaves the student in a state of fear. Shooting for perfection means that we cannot ask for help. We have to adopt a veneer of invulnerability. This begins the fortress behind which many future physicians reside."[32]

The Sequelae of *Special*

How does *special* impact us when we finally begin our careers as doctors? This veneer of perfection and invulnerability can alienate the people we work with. Overemphasis on being the "expert" and having the right answer—combined with these aforementioned complexities in medical training and a large incoming class of trainees who have been dealt the *special* card—can lead to some physicians who are quite full of themselves!

That brings us back to Dan, now a 51-year-old internist sent to coaching by his practice manager because of difficulty getting along with others.

When Dan first came to me for coaching, I was actually impressed by what a likable guy he was—friendly, congenial. Maybe a little bit full of himself, sure, but I found myself wondering what his practice manager was so concerned about. She had told me what an egotist he was, how condescending he could be, and how many of her staff were sick and tired of working with him. While I didn't doubt her words, I found it difficult to imagine Dan acting in the ways she described.

But the data told no lies.

Dan's patient satisfaction scores were in the bottom quartile for his department, and staff complaints numbered in the dozens. He was known to be a top-notch physician. That was not the problem. What *was* problematic was that multiple staff found him difficult to get along with. They described him as condescending, abrupt, and more than a little egotistical. One nurse said she constantly felt put down by Dan. Another described him as "a smarty-pants on steroids."

There was also the episode the prior summer where Dan lost it with Saeed from IT, going from calm to shouting when, after four hours of Dan being frustrated at not being able to get charts done or respond to inbox messages, Saeed rapidly found that the problem was simply a cord that Dan had plugged into the wrong port.

You can see that Dan had been triggered into shouting merely by a sense of being one-upped by "some guy" from IT.

Though this was all bad enough from the view of his practice manager, worse yet were the complaints from patients. More than a few had given him low scores in their satisfaction surveys, with comments such as "full of himself," "arrogant," and "uncaring."

It came to a head one Friday when Dan was seeing an elderly patient who had brought her granddaughter, a nursing student, along for the visit. Dan was busy explaining how he was going to deal with the patient's abnormal thyroid tests when the granddaughter interrupted and started telling her grandmother her own version of how this was impacting her health. Each time Dan tried to return to his plan, the granddaughter again chimed in.

It was near the end of Dan's day, after a long week of complicated patients, and he was tired. He found himself feeling frustrated and annoyed. After all, how could this underling be upstaging his expertise? Without realizing it, he rolled his eyes, and out came the words: "Oh, so *you're* the doctor now, are you?"

It was this, the last on a long list of complaints, that sent Dan to me for 6 months of coaching. Behind the actions that resulted in each of these complaints—yet hidden from his view—was Dan's identity as *special*.

On top of identifying as being special, medical training can exacerbate some of the maladaptive traits that medical trainees enter with. While being a bit perfectionistic, self-focused, and overly hard on yourself can get you into medical school and through it, these patterns do very little to sustain you as a practicing physician.

Moreover, our sense of being special can impact the entire healthcare team. As Harvard leader Tom Lee summed up in a *Harvard Business Review* article, "Working in teams does not come easily to physicians, who still often see themselves as heroic lone healers...Doctors have historically seen themselves as their patients' sole advocates, with the rest of the world divided into those who are helping and those who are in the way...Some of my most respected colleagues have confessed a wish that no one would even talk to their patients except through them."[33]

Perhaps our sense of our own importance keeps us from leaning in to what other members of the healthcare team can offer. Instead of appreciating the unique strengths nurses, advanced practice providers, and other non-physicians bring to the healthcare endeavor, our sense of being special can leave us deriding their expertise. Instead of embracing the fact that it takes an entire team to provide excellent care, we feel intruded upon. After all, we have internalized a belief that we alone are special.

Sadly, this can end up hurting us all.

Problems, Problems, Everywhere

Medical training takes insecure, perfectionistic young people and trains them to double down on a mindset that can be near-incapacitating: The diagnostic mindset.

Importantly, a key aspect of medical training is learning to diagnose. When a patient comes in with new-onset back pain, for example, it's our job to figure out what might be causing it. Making sense out of their constellation of symptoms, we ponder this diagnosis and that; then we pronounce our diagnosis and prescribe a treatment. The problem needs to be identified so that a solution can be provided.

This is obviously the backbone of medicine and exactly how doctors should be trained to think. The problem is that this mental pattern of seeking out problems to be labeled and solved is difficult to shut off. And without mindful training, it can be the lens through which doctors see everything in their lives: As a problem to be solved—or worse, as an imperfection, and thus a threat to their very identity.

Spending 70–80 hours a week under extreme pressure and stress diagnosing, solving, studying, correcting, and living and breathing black-and-white, right-or-wrong, problem and solution thinking forces doctors-to-be into this survival, problem-focused orientation.

Excessive use of this lens, part of what I call the "fixed medical mindset," is a core element of the perfectionism fostered in medical training, with an emphasis on diagnosing and fixing that creates a highly critical mind. At the same time, however, it isn't a switch that physicians are taught to shut off beyond work—and it is one that many physicians wind up applying to themselves.

A young, anxious doctor-to-be who spends all day trying to get multiple-choice questions right often tries to live life the same way, as if the lens has narrowed to the point that everything is seen as a problem to be fixed. We see patients as problems, healthcare as a problem, and even our very lives and relationships as a group of problems that we need to fix or solve. Sadly, this wreaks havoc with our lives, both within and outside of our careers. Conversations with loved ones become problems to be solved, conflicts become threats to one's identity, and life problems, like clinical ones, are often approached with a perfectionistic tendency.

> Can you relate to being hyper-focused on "diagnosing" and trying to fix yourself and those around you? How often do you find yourself focused on being right and trying to live your life and work perfectly?

Increasingly, physicians are publicly acknowledging that, in the face of the drive for invulnerability and perfectionism, any perceived flaw or mistake made with a patient readily becomes a threat to their identity.[34] These insecurities—coupled with the excessive comparisons, ratings, and rankings—push physicians toward burnout, losing the motivation, energy, and idealism that characterized their pursuit of a medical career in the first place.[35]

As you're reading this, you may be thinking that not focusing on a problem creates the risk of letting things fall through the cracks. You would be correct. Many times, it is critically important to focus on what is broken or not going well. For example,

focusing on the defects in medical devices can help a team elim-
inate them. Looking at the percentage of physicians not washing
their hands between patients led to improvements in processes.
Identifying low measles vaccination rates in African nations
was necessary for the World Health Organization to implement
improvements. There are many important instances where a
problem-focused lens and analytical thinking will be necessary.

The problem (pun intended) is that we don't learn how to be
selective about when we apply this lens, and when carried to an
extreme, the problem-focused lens actually creates further problems. Directed, intentional analysis of a flaw in a methodology
is crucial to correcting and learning from it. But unintentional,
unconscious analysis of every aspect of our life and its perceived
imperfections is where this lens often ends up running our lives.

The brain is naturally wired to seek out problems and perceived survival threats. But in 2023, this lens often operates in
overdrive. And that's **before** medical training—practically conditioning doctors-to-be to become paranoid balls of stress. In Part
II of this book, we'll explore a key mindfulness and neuroscience
concept—that what you focus on becomes your reality. An excessive focus on problems creates an existence where it seems like
nothing is going right—a perfect breeding ground for burnout.
When we are unrested or in a situation that our mind perceives
to be life-or-death (read: many medical school exams), this problem-focused lens naturally intensifies.

Fortunately, the wellness of medical students and residents is
now recognized as an area of concern, and examples of positive
efforts are many.[36–40]

In 2003, the Accreditation Council for Graduate Medical Education adopted a maximum of 80 hours per week for interns and residents. This heralded a dramatic shift toward recognizing that physicians, like all others, need sleep—not only to perform well, but also for their own mental and physical well-being. In response to high levels of burnout, the National Board for Medical Education, the National Academy of Medicine, the American Association of Medical Colleges, the Accreditation Council for Graduate Medical Education, and the American Medical Association—indeed, almost every professional society—has taken steps to address the topic of trainee wellness (see the Notes section for multiple examples).[41]

While necessary and well-intentioned, these interventions don't change the multiple problematic factors in training, namely the push for perfection and invulnerability, comparisons and pimping, and lack of training on how to be judicious in using the problem-focused lens.

In other words, **many wellness measures are addressing the symptoms of burnout, but not the cause**. There is clearly much room for improvement.

Diagnosing What's Right

On Monday mornings for the past decade, I head to my hospital, one of Harvard's most prestigious (*special* strikes again!), to teach residents about mindfulness and resilience. On this particular Monday, Emilia, Josh, and I gathered in a small windowless room. These residents are members of the BBC club—Brilliant But Clueless—and they were skeptical that this white-haired woman could impart anything they didn't already know.

I began by asking how they were doing around well-being.

Not missing a beat, Emilia said, "Not well." She was feeling like an imposter. "It's not even a thought process; it's completely true. I *am* an imposter," she said with vehemence, sure that her proclamation was the truth. "I feel like it's only a matter of time until I screw up with patients and then everybody knows." Eyes welling up with tears, she paused. "Maybe I shouldn't even be here at all."

Josh chimed in, saying that his top resilience challenge was "a pervasive sense of inadequacy." He said it was almost impossible to see that he had any strengths at all, and he was sure that he didn't.

The room was completely devoid of energy.

Then I asked them to tell me what was going well.

I was initially met with silence. But after a bit of prodding, I got something out of them.

Josh had recently gotten engaged, and his parents had happily retired to Florida. He was learning about sports injuries, which fascinated him, and his name was going to be on a forthcoming case publication.

Emilia had just celebrated her little sister's high school graduation, where her sister proclaimed to the family how much of an inspiration Emilia was. Emilia had also recently set a personal record for the deadlift (she's an avid powerlifter) and had gotten through a difficult ICU rotation, earning her a favorable review for the field she hoped to enter.

As they spoke, the room began to lighten, and I could see both of them feeling proud and energized. (I guess their white-haired professor knew a little something after all!)

It's ironic, but as this example demonstrates, the more we focus on what we're doing wrong or poorly, the less energy we have to actually go and fix it. Perfectionism and the excessive focus on problems keep us from acknowledging what's going right in our lives and serve to deplete us of our energy. The more we focus on what we're doing right, and what's going well in our lives, the more confident and whole we feel, and the more the little missteps start to melt away.

> Try it yourself—take a minute to give yourself credit for everything that's going well. Just like Emilia and Josh, it might take some effort, but you'll likely experience the same buoyancy these young trainees experienced.

The End Result

The result of an emphasis on perfectionism, comparisons, a problem-focused diagnostic mindset, invulnerability, and not spending enough time diagnosing what is right is that physicians develop a stress-, shame-, and fear-based approach to their work.[42-46] Instead of being rewarded for trying their best and striving for excellence, the future physician becomes trapped in patterns of judgment, harsh self-criticism, reactive defensiveness, and fear of making a mistake. This takes us out of touch with our natural curiosity, open-mindedness, and desire to learn and grow. These patterns are profoundly demotivating, de-energizing, and counterproductive to caring for ourselves—and for others. Additionally, they exacerbate the challenge of adapting to a changing healthcare environment.

Training also leaves us unable to trust in ourselves and our abilities. It leaves us confused about our values and about our very sense of meaning and purpose. Any trace of an internal compass of knowing and self-validation is pushed aside, perhaps even paved over. In fact, by the end of training, this internal compass of achievement and success has been replaced by an external one. Do this right, and you will be a success. Always have the answer and never show vulnerability, and you can remain in the club.

In many ways, medical training can almost be thought of as a fairy tale about the development of the physician. An idealistic young man or woman has a dream of caring for others, of rising above difficulty, of moving to a lofty place in society where their value will be seen and cherished. But to get there, many sacrifices needs to be made—battles fought, moats crossed, others bested.

Then they get to the other side and receive the crown of glory, only to find that the castle is not the large, inspiring place they imagined. Instead, the rooms are small, there's dust about, and many walls are in need of repair.

At the same time, the cost of reaching the castle is extraordinarily high. It may not be the death-defying journey of the would-be knight, but the chronic stress generated in the process takes a toll on the mind and body of the future physician. It leaves us in a depleted and brittle state, a state in which we now enter our career as a full-fledged physician.

While not true for all, many physicians unconsciously learn to inhabit a stance of survival, needing to be vigilant to threat. Fear activates the primitive parts of the brain, keeping the physician protective, walled off, and shut down. This is the opposite of a place of curiosity, caring, connection, compassion, and service.

Tragically, we can end up living in a small version of our full selves.

Importantly, what's lost is a sense of the true larger self that each of us is at our core: A fully caring and committed person who entered training deeply concerned about the well-being of others.

By the end of training, we find ourselves:

- Perfectionistic
- Hypercritical and focused on our shortcomings
- Disconnected from our inner values and purpose
- Rejecting our inner wisdom and resourcefulness
- Overwhelmed and exhausted

These patterns are a perfect breeding ground for burnout. Instead of fostering the powerful tools of mindfulness and self-regulation to get past these hurdles, physicians-to-be are implicitly taught to just work harder and harder.

It's no wonder so many of us leave our training already burned out.

A Mindful Approach

Moving past these patterns takes small, intentional, mindful tweaks that most of us were never taught how to make. We can unwire the mental patterns that leave us predisposed to stress, anxiety, burnout, and self-criticism. We can take the good from our medical training and leave the rest, and we can shift from fear and perfectionism to compassion and joy.

When we learn to apply mindful awareness to the impact of training, we can begin to see and alter the resultant patterns in ourselves. We can move the bar from perfect to good enough. We can start to admit that we don't have everything figured out and learn to become more comfortable with imperfection. Ironically, the more we learn to do so, the more productive and fulfilled we can be. And happy, *Mindful MDs* are better physicians—more caring, more compassionate, and more present with both their patients and their loved ones.

This is quite the opposite of what we were taught, but we can start to accept the foibles of being human—shortcomings, vulnerabilities, and all. This can actually help us step into the career fulfillment we've worked so hard to achieve.

We can shift to a more empowered stance, using the difficulties we face as substrate for learning and growth. We can realize that we don't have to wait for something outside ourselves to change in order to achieve happiness and satisfaction, and we can move from a fixed medical mindset to a truly growth-oriented approach. We can shift out of beliefs that tie our identity to something other than our true inner core. We can reverse the fear- and shame-based stance learned in our training and embrace our natural curiosity and love of learning.

We can get to a place where we can thrive in our lives and work.

We'll begin this journey back into balance in the second part of this book, looking at 6 ways mindfulness helps physicians (and others) restore autonomy, cure burnout, and truly get our lives back.

Q AND A

1. I know many physicians who don't have the arrogant sense of being special you describe. Is it fair to generalize in this way?

You are definitely correct, as I also know many humble physicians. In this chapter, I am drawing upon examples to illustrate a phenomenon that operates in an unconscious way for many physicians. What I have found interesting is that when I bring up the concept of being special with colleagues, many experience a powerful "aha" moment.

At the same time, *special* is not a universal mindset and also doesn't show up the same way for every physician. Many physicians can take *special* in the other direction, feeling less than everyone around them and expressing excessive humility. Either way, this pattern often runs in the background.

Just like my mindless moment on the flight, I needed to evoke mindfulness to bring my own sense of feeling special out into the light of day before I could even see the ways it was impacting my behavior. Once I did so, I could observe it for what it was and question my own automatic and unconscious patterning. With that power of observation, I began to see that I could let go of my sense of being special, as it was something I carried with a type of hubris that was out of my field of view. Doing so has allowed me to interact with others with much greater interest, ease, and presence, as well as greater respect for their unique qualities and contributions.

2. I'm not a doctor, but after reading this chapter, I could see similar patterns in myself. What makes you think the issue of being special is unique to doctors?

These patterns are not the sole purview of doctors. Anyone can experience being labeled, and thus internalize, an identity as special, along with the subsequent impact on their life and work. Special can be linked to academic achievement or just about any area where we depend on external recognition and being different than those around us. While doctors are especially prone to this, anyone can find themselves going through life like this.

This kind of labeling is unfortunate because it can set us on a path of thinking that we are different from others. Whether we are labeled "better than" or "less than," there can be the same detrimental impact we have seen in this chapter—insecurity and dependence on others to validate our self-worth.

Nonetheless, this pattern is an important one for physicians to identify in themselves since it impacts how we relate to others, our own quality of life, and our risk for burnout.

3. You write that perfectionism is the enemy of the good, as well as of well-being and resilience. That may be true, but isn't excellent, error-free medicine what we must aim for?

This is a great question. In an ideal world, there would be no mistakes made. But, in the real world, human beings are imperfect. Human error occurs. At the same time, when we expect perfection, it puts a level of stress on physicians that can actually keep us from doing what we can all do, which is our very best. It turns out that this very pressure leaves physicians experiencing fear. As we'll explore, fear activates the primitive parts of the brain and shuts off the higher brain, the prefrontal cortex. It's a little bit of a chicken-and-egg cycle, but our own brain circuitry means that perfectionism can actually backfire.

Mindfulness doesn't involve a slackening of standards. Instead, it fosters calm, steadiness, and focus—essential ingredients for anyone's optimal performance, whether physician, pilot, or parent. These qualities are what truly promote excellence in medicine and reduce the likelihood of errors occurring.

By approaching diagnoses with calm curiosity, and taking our self-worth and fear out of the equation, we can bring more compassion to our patients, let go of fear, anxiety, and other negative emotions that cloud our view, and make critical decisions from a place of greater calm and focus.

4. If there are so many problems with medical education, why hasn't anything changed?

Change in medical culture tends to happen slowly. But the good news is that many changes *have* been made. When I was in training, I was often on call every third night, had a closet-sized call room in the middle of a noisy hospital floor to sleep in, and had to manage when getting next to no rest. This meant that working 100–110 hours per week was not uncommon. While 80 hours per week is still a lot, it is a significant improvement.

Additionally, I don't wish to disregard the tremendous efforts underway to improve trainee and attending physician wellness. What I am drawing attention to is that these need to go deeper, as they do not get to the heart of the problematic patterns physicians learn in their training. Although they are important, they don't help physicians get to some of the roots of burnout, which are the thought and behavioral patterns that training fosters and reinforces.

As you'll learn in Part II, mindfulness provides a way for us to see these problematic patterns more clearly and gives us the tools to correct them at their core.

Lastly, not every aspect of medical training is bad. We have a dysfunctional healthcare system, but that system is powered by countless highly talented and dedicated physicians. Our training definitely produces great doctors, and I'm sure you are one of them. What mindfulness helps us do is let go of the burdens our training saddled us with, while also allowing us to hold on to the vast knowledge and skills we gained. From there, we can return to the curiosity and compassion we started our medical journeys with. We can become fully integrated and thriving *Mindful MDs*.

PART II: 6 MINDFUL WAYS

"Mindfulness means being awake. It means knowing what you are doing."
—Jon Kabat-Zinn

Now that we've deepened our understanding of the factors that set us up for burnout, it's time to get to the heart of why you picked up this book—getting you out of it.

Part II of this book will serve as a comprehensive deep dive into unwinding and reshaping the mental patterns that set us up for burnout.

We'll go deep into the tricks our minds play on us and cover actionable strategies to get our minds to quiet down. We'll learn how to choose which of the stories our minds spin are helpful, and how to selectively ignore the ones that are not.

In short, we'll see how to remove the big internal hurdles that are keeping you stuck and sapping your energy. Once those are gone, you'll get back in touch with compassion, purpose, and presence and will be set up for upward spirals and enjoying your life beyond burnout.

Tactically, you'll learn 6 key ways mindfulness helps you restore your autonomy and makes burnout a thing of the past:

1. **Recognize That You Are Not Your Thoughts**
2. **Step Out Of Mental Stories**
3. **Reduce Reactivity**
4. **Lean Into Compassion, Connection, and Purpose**
5. **Work With What Is**
6. **Cultivate Upward Spirals**

1. RECOGNIZE THAT YOU ARE NOT YOUR THOUGHTS

"The mind is a wonderful servant but a terrible master."
—Robin Sharma

For Mira, the inner chatter started when her alarm buzzed at 5:15 a.m.—and it was anything but calm and friendly.

When she didn't get out of bed to exercise: *I'm such a slug. Why can't I have the self-discipline other physicians have? I've never had what it takes.*

When her 17-year-old daughter, Ella, wasn't getting her homework done: *What am I going to do about her grades? Maybe I should get her a tutor, but tutors cost a lot, and I need to save for college. My ex is making this so difficult. I can't believe he's resisting paying support again. What an idiot I was to marry him in the first place!*

When her 13-year-old, Dina, yelled at Ella to stop snooping in her diary: *Why can't they get along the way my sister's kids do? The two of them are making my life miserable. I can't stand these mornings. They completely stress me out.*

When traffic was jammed on her way to work: *Why is everyone driving so slowly? I hate my commute. What was I thinking by moving to a practice so far away? Maybe I should quit and look for something closer to home. If I was only home more, Ella wouldn't be having all these problems.*

When she arrived late to her office, facing a difficult patient and another double-booked morning: *It's completely unfair that I have to see so many patients. Now that it's all about patient satisfaction, this is what I have to put up with. I have the worst luck of anyone. I can't stand it when patients like her are on my schedule. I'll never get my charts done now. How am I ever going to get through another day like this?*

Not even 3 hours into her day, Mira already felt overwhelmed.

While it seemed clear to Mira that it was her daughters, her ex, the commute, and the office schedule to blame for her overwhelm, that was actually only a partial truth. Her life circumstances as a physician and single mom were complicated. It's no easy thing raising teenagers, being a busy physician, and meeting the demands of an overbooked panel of patients—a daily juggling act anyone would find stressful.

But the difficulties of Mira's existence were multiplied by the soundtrack of thoughts that played in the background of her days.

What We Don't Learn

Our minds are extremely busy places. Thought upon thought is how most of us go through our days. All these thoughts overlay our actual experience and, without awareness, become our experience. What goes on in our minds literally becomes the world we see.

For longevity in a stressful career like medicine, it is vital to learn to work with your own mind—it is truly the most important instrument you'll ever operate.

Unfortunately, medical school doesn't teach us how to do so.

In fact, the medical school curriculum is dominated by the vast amount of specific knowledge needed to practice medicine: Findings on complex biochemical pathways, the physiology of the heart and lungs, and even issues as esoteric and detailed as acid-base imbalances in the kidney.

But we don't learn how to manage mornings like Mira's. Alongside the core curriculum of symptoms and studies, we learn next to nothing about how we work, how we react, how to manage the complex emotions we experience, how to take care of ourselves and avoid burnout, and how to cope with all the change and uncertainty of the healthcare landscape.[1-2] At the core of this is self-awareness and self-management, the foundation of mindfulness.

In all the hours spent on acquiring knowledge, little to no time is spent on how to manage our minds. Yet, our minds and the thoughts they produce form the portal through which we experience *everything*. This portal is the complex filter through which all incoming data is processed, and it dictates the learning, growing, understanding, and interpreting of all that we experience. And quite often, as was the case for Mira, what the mind generates are draining, fear-based overgeneralizations that do not always reflect the reality in front of us.

The first key to managing this complex instrument is recognizing that you are not your thoughts—the first way mindfulness restores your autonomy and cures healthcare burnout.

Training the Mind

Let me take a step back and explain what mindfulness is.

First and foremost, it's the complete toolkit to managing your most important instrument as a physician (and as a human): Your mind.

A more traditional definition is that **mindfulness is our capacity for awareness—conscious, open, receptive, and purposeful awareness—of what is occurring in the present moment**. It involves utilizing this awareness to train our minds to *shift away* from the thoughts that most of us are preoccupied with and *shift toward* what we are actually experiencing, rather than our thoughts about our experience. It involves training our minds to shift toward the reality of what's happening in the present moment, the one that is occurring right now. At its core, it is a way of being and relating to ourselves, our circumstances, one another, and the world around us.

With mindfulness, we are training ourselves in our ways of thinking, feeling, and behaving. We are training ourselves to see which of our thoughts are helpful and which are not. We're training our minds to be less attached to the unhelpful ones, to let them pass through without giving them as much of our attention. A core part of this detachment is recognizing that the randomly generated blurbs created by our minds aren't us.

With mindfulness, we are training ourselves to become the master of our minds, a skill that is especially important for physicians.

Mira, like most of us, was anything but.

Without this training, we are like a boat adrift at sea. We don't have an anchor or a compass to steady and guide us. We don't have the tools to right our thinking or manage the complex emotions that arise in our stressful lives and work. In a sense, our mind is allowed to run wild. We are left prey to our circumstances, without what we need to work with them. We are left reacting to everything that occurs around us. For many physicians, this means having few tools to manage all the instability, change, uncertainty, moral distress, and turmoil a career in healthcare now involves.

The good news is that these are tools mindfulness provides.

Getting to Know the Busy Mind

Although we haven't learned to pay close attention to what's going on inside our minds, *we can*. When we do, we learn a few important things, including just how busy the human mind can be.

We humans produce between 6,000 and 20,000 thoughts per day, and at times it can feel like even more.[3-4] At the low end, assuming we're awake for 16 hours, that means over 375 thoughts per hour or more than 6 per minute. At the high end, we're talking about over 20 per minute—or one every 3 seconds. In fact, in a somewhat unsavory analogy, we can liken the human mind to the salivary glands, constantly producing thoughts. With this analogy, we see that while thought is both natural and essential, it is highly problematic when overproduced.

Perhaps you're skeptical of these claims and are thinking: *This might be true for others, but not for me.*

Take a moment to see for yourself in this mini exercise.

Put this book down, set your phone timer for 2 minutes, and count your thoughts. You can even imagine that you're like a cat, sitting expectantly at a mousehole, ready to pounce each time a thought appears in your mind.

How many thoughts did you have? I suspect it was more than a few.

With groups of physicians, I've heard anywhere from 4 to 100. And that's just in 2 minutes. Multiply that maximum by 16 hours of wakefulness, and it's up to 48,000 thoughts a day. It's no surprise that many physicians have difficulty quieting their minds!

Now, this onslaught of thoughts can be damning, helpful, or a slight annoyance, depending on how we relate to it. With mindfulness, we're not trying to turn off the flow of thoughts. Those new to the practice often mistakenly assume that is the goal. Even if we tried, we wouldn't be able to stop thoughts from occurring—even Buddhist monks who have spent a lifetime training do not have silent minds. Thoughts are what the mind produces, plain and simple. Instead, with mindfulness, we're getting to know our thoughts—and recognizing them for what they are.

For physicians, useful thoughts are myriad:

This rash means Lyme disease.

That abnormal mammogram needs follow-up.

The correct dose of lisinopril is 10 milligrams, not 100 milligrams.

What if that murmur is mitral regurgitation?

But these useful thoughts are often tiny daisies sprouting up in a field full of weeds.

Our thoughts can take us down dark alleys of worry, rumination, and fear. We can spin off in annoyance or frustration about the ways the practice of medicine has changed. We can get caught in a worry that we're going to be sued for missing a key diagnosis. As author Anne Lamott jests, "My mind is like a bad neighborhood. I try not to go there alone."[5]

We can find our minds having repetitive thoughts:

No one sees how hard I'm working.

The practice of medicine has gone to hell in a handbasket.

Those administrators are ruining healthcare.

This isn't what I signed up for.

We can also find ourselves having internal arguments with someone, like our practice administrator or a family member, who isn't even there. Many times, our minds second-guess, spin stories, and overthink issues large and small.

You may not be fully conscious of this operating in the background but, like Mira, find yourself exhausted, irritable, and reactive with those around you. Your thoughts don't occur in a vacuum, after all, they profoundly impact your mood and behavior. Especially when you identify with them.

Like a Monkey

In mindfulness, we call this incessant pattern of thinking "monkey mind." Imagine a large group of monkeys swinging from branch to branch, chattering away to one another as they wildly grab the next banana. Imagine the quality of frenetic, loud, constant energy this scene involves.

Does this sound anything like a description of your own mind?

In addition to enabling us to see this mental busyness more clearly, mindfulness also helps us spot the unhelpful thoughts our minds are busy producing. These come in a variety of forms.

One of the core forms of the monkey mind, which Mira fell victim to, is judgments. Typically, not very positive ones at that: *This day is awful. He can be so stupid at times. I am too fat. I don't like her.*

Worries and rumination dominate another category of our thoughts: *What if this doesn't work out? I wish I hadn't said that. What if I can't get my charts done on time? What if things get even worse?* You may recognize that this is the category that often wakes us up during the night, making it difficult to return to sleep.

Then there are the planning and rehearsing thoughts: *When I get home, I'll change into comfortable clothes. We should book that flight today. When I meet with my boss tomorrow, I need to make sure she sees what a good worker I am.*

Further, many of our thoughts are about ourselves. When we pay attention, we become aware of just how much the frame revolves around us, as a good proportion of our thoughts include I, me, and my: *I should be happier. My work is too demanding. I wish I was thinner. This is not going well for me.*

This self-referential pattern is the way the human mind is constructed. Yet, when we focus on these self-occupied, judgmental thoughts without questioning them, we can fall into habits that make us (and those around us) miserable.

We can see this in the case of Brian, a 57-year-old thoracic surgeon sent to coaching after complaints from nurses that he was condescending, abrupt, and rude. There were also complaints from patients, who reported a similar tone.

A product of four years of college, four years of medical school, five years of general surgery residency, and two years of thoracic surgery fellowship, Brian had learned that he was the captain of the team—the boss—and that it was his opinion that mattered. His training had cemented the proverbial "my way or the highway" attitude.

And how was this working for him and his workplace relationships? Interestingly enough, Brian hadn't stopped to consider whether it was working or not. In fact, he had never considered the opinions nurses had about him as important. After all, he was the boss, so what did their opinions matter anyway?

So when his chief relayed the complaints, Brian reacted with hostility. "What are they complaining about? Everyone knows I'm an excellent surgeon. Who cares if I'm easy to get along with? They're all just a bunch of wusses. Can't they see all the good I'm doing for the hospital?"

But Brian, like most physicians, had a deep love of learning. That was what had led him to a career in surgery in the first place. Additionally, he wanted to do better but simply didn't know how.

Since Brian's pattern of thinking was unseen to him, we needed to bring it into mindful awareness. To this end, I tasked Brian with spending 2 weeks paying attention to his thoughts. But it didn't take 2 weeks. After just 3 days, he called me to say, "What on earth is going on up there? It's like a crazy town with all the thoughts I'm having! I had no idea my mind was so busy."

He was also completely shocked to discover how many of his thoughts were judgments about what was not going well.

Brian's learning did not stop there.

Brian shared a pattern he now saw was part of the reason for the complaints. He told me that he used to walk around his hospital, intently looking for things that were not working well. Like Dan, Brian's high intellectual abilities had led to being labeled early on as the smart and special one. Between that and having been taught to be the problem-focused captain of the health-care team, he had learned that it was his job to identify flaws and institute a fix. In an almost unconscious way, he had charged himself with making a mental checklist of his findings and then ensuring that everybody knew about each and every problem he identified.

Sadly, this kept Brian trapped in a pattern of negativity and judgment. Coworkers bore the brunt of this hypercritical approach, but his patients suffered too. While grateful knowing they were in expert hands, they often left his office with a sense that he was overly full of himself and less concerned about them than about being the expert who had the answers.

Once Brian brought his pattern into mindful awareness, it did not take long for him to see that it was his own behavior that was creating the negative impression. Now, the complaints he'd received began to make more sense.

Equally important, through our coaching he began to notice how all this judging showed up in his body. He noticed that he was holding himself tightly, brow furrowed, shoulders raised, back tense. The combined mental and physical pattern was making him into a tightly wound, finger-wagging judge, viewing everything in a rigid, demanding, and negative way.

One day, Brian came to his coaching session with a powerful observation: "I'm beginning to see now that I've had too high of an opinion of my own opinion." With the same clarity and objectivity he had when diagnosing an invasive lung tumor, Brian now saw exactly how his own pattern worked. Additionally, he knew this was not how he wanted to be acting. As his mindfulness lens widened, he could see exactly what he needed to excise, just as expertly as he would excise a malignant mass.

Lost in Thought

The constant battering of thoughts can impact physicians in different ways.

Natalia, a 51-year-old psychiatrist, was extremely devoted to her patients. While most psychiatrists now focus on medication management, Natalia focused on listening to and supporting her patients. She sought coaching, however, after realizing that her mind was so busy that she couldn't truly focus on what her patients were saying.

Alexandria, a busy early-career primary care internist, typically stayed late to return patients' calls and left work each day with many charts to complete. She'd get home, eat dinner, and then try to spend time with her 5-year-old daughter. But her mind was still focused on work, worried about the patients she'd seen that day or the charts still to be done.

Even when her daughter was snuggling in her lap, sweetly telling Alexandria about her dolls or the friends she'd made on the playground, Alexandria's mind was so busy that she could barely feel the sensation of her daughter on her skin. She realized, with tremendous guilt, that she wasn't really listening to her daughter's words.

For both Natalia and Alexandria, the busyness of their minds was distracting them from being present—not just with patients but with loved ones as well. They were lost in a world of thought, missing what was happening right in front of them.

Not simply lost in thought, both also spent considerable amounts of time and energy beating themselves up over being lost in thought. This kind of "feeding fire with fire" is a perfect recipe for burnout and for not being present in the unfolding moments of our lives.

Perhaps this is something you can relate to.

In realizing that we are not our thoughts, it is helpful to realize just how ephemeral our thoughts are. In fact, they are simply transient mental events and nothing more.

When you pause and consider it, you'll see that no thought you've ever had has lasted. None! Our thoughts are similar to the clouds in the sky. They arise, pass through, and dissipate. Some are like storm clouds: Ominous, heavy, and potent. Others are light and wispy and move through without turbulence. At the moment they occur, thoughts seem to have so much substance, yet they do not. When we let them, they pass right by.

The mind's interpretive processes are complex, and sometimes our minds are sticky—almost like flypaper for certain types of thoughts. Observing your thoughts, you'll likely notice that many of your thoughts include fear and worry or replaying things that didn't go well or might not go well in the future, with far fewer about the positives in the past, present, or future. The brain's negativity bias means that our thoughts tend to drift (and stick) more in a downward direction than up.

Why are our brains so predisposed to negativity? Well, in prehistoric times, fear and worry were essential survival tools. Being able to recognize threats became the difference between surviving an attacking saber-toothed tiger and not. Today, the threats we face may not be as visceral as the apex predators of the past, but unfortunately, we're stuck with the same programming: A brain hyper-focused on judging almost everything it encounters and determining what's wrong, which in modern times tends to be psychological, as opposed to physical, threats.

Judgments, Judgments, Judgments

Let's return to our challenging (but committed to improving) friend, Brian. As you read about him, you probably saw that many of his thoughts involved judgments, and negative ones at that. It turns out that this is the case for most of us.

In some ways, it's as if our mind has a type of filter: Assessing everything coming its way, getting stuck on the negatives, and allowing the positives to flow right through. Of course, judgments are a key aspect of a physician's mind. After all, we are in the business of diagnosing.

Mindfulness is not about shedding this important skill. Instead, by paying attention, we become more discerning about when we are applying this diagnostic lens and how much attention we give our diagnoses and judgments. Part of that discernment is noticing how the mind tends to label things as good, bad, or neutral. Once these labels are affixed, something interesting occurs.

When we label something as good, we want more of it. When labeled bad, we push it away. When labeled neutral, the mind simply stops paying attention to it. All this mental labeling and reacting takes energy and leaves the mind responding to almost every stimulus it encounters. A day full of these micro-reactions leaves us with little energy to simply enjoy whatever is in front of us.

Additionally, when we're unaware of how judgments are influencing our behavior, it's as if we, like Brian and Mira, are just along for the ride. Like a marionette reacting to a puppeteer, we readily become trapped by these fairly automatic judgments and reactions.

Mindfulness invites us to experience life without all the automatic judgment. It invites us to see that these judgments are simply the mind's attempt to make sense of the world around us. Dropping them helps us place our attention more on what is actually occurring. For Alexandria, this meant the precious time with her young daughter. For Brian, it meant seeing that much in his hospital was going well.

When we step out of all the judgments and labels, in fact, what we experience can be tremendously refreshing. It can also make us much more resourceful in our interactions with others. This has particular significance for busy physicians.

To take this idea further, you've likely had the experience of thinking something is going to be bad and then it actually isn't. When your teenager takes the car to the nearby mall, for example, saying they'll be back in an hour and you don't hear anything for three, your mind may imagine something horrible. You picture an awful car accident, your cortisol levels rise, and panic starts setting in. But then they return, casually shrugging off your concern and accusing you of being the worst helicopter parent in the neighborhood.

When we step away from all the judgments, we begin to appreciate that our minds are not always the best predictors. Besides, all the stress created by the anticipatory fear, worry, and dread this erroneous thinking causes is not always necessary.

It's quite costly too. For Brian, the cost in terms of poor relationships was high.

Similarly, those things the mind labels as neutral, and not of interest, can actually be important and worth taking in. For instance, on your morning commute, you may be driving along, your mind so preoccupied worrying about what's going to happen at work, that you miss the spring trees and their beautiful lush colors. Or, like Alexandria, the busy primary care mom, your mind may be so busy thinking about patients or charting that you miss out on precious moments with your child.

At the same time, with the clarity forged through mindfulness, we begin to see things more as they truly are, not as our mind tells us they are. Further, since things are not always bad until our minds label them so, we can reduce the stress caused by all of this unnecessary labeling. Very importantly, reducing judgment rights the physician's problem-focused, perfectionistic lens and helps us be more satisfied with what we have right here, right now—as opposed to the dissatisfaction that comes with the almost endless discord created by the judging mind.

After all, when we pay greater attention, we begin to see that judging many things as bad only serves to fuel frustration, annoyance, and impatience, squandering our precious time and energy and predisposing us to burnout.

The Inner Narrator

As we expand our mindful awareness, we also begin to realize there is a narrator-like figure inside our mind that is constantly speaking to us—about ourselves, our experience, and the world we inhabit. The narrator is telling us where to move, who to speak to, if a situation is going to be good or bad, or if we're doing too much of this, too little of that.

While the natural tendency is to identify with this chatter, try imagining that this motor-mouthed narrator is a roommate. A generally decent soul, but one who won't shut up. They sit too close to you, tell you you're bad at your job, say your nose is too big, and imply that your sister's a better parent than you are—and they make similar judgments about everyone and everything you encounter. It's pretty likely that you wouldn't tolerate this behavior, would you?

Yet, when we pay attention, we begin to see that this is exactly what our mind is doing throughout many waking moments of our days.

I love this analogy for two reasons: (1) It has been illuminating for the physicians I've coached—a great representation of the sheer frequency of thoughts occurring—and (2) it reminds us that our thoughts (read: our inner narrators) aren't us.

This kind of framing is important, as it helps create a distance, or gap, between ourselves and our thoughts. While this gap may occupy only a second of time, it is critical in developing autonomy over our minds.

This gap creates a space where we can recognize that many of our thoughts are misperceptions, incorrect appraisals, or things we believe will happen but never actually do. Sometimes, they are even outright falsehoods.

The gap gives us room to see this.

But medical training doesn't teach us to stop and question whether our thoughts are correct. We learn to take our thoughts seriously and believe they are facts.

When we pause and question them, however, we see that this is far from true. In actuality, we can be so wedded to our thoughts that, like Natalia and Alexandria, we don't pay attention to what's actually in front of us. This was the case when Brian made his daily rounds. He simply had not learned to question what his inner narrator was telling him.

While these mind patterns are a common experience for all, they are particularly costly for physicians. In Brian's case, his mental patterns were impacting both coworkers and patients.

The good news is that we can learn to stop and question our thoughts. We can develop the ability to work with our thoughts in a productive way. When we utilize mindfulness to move away from the narrator into the present moments of our lives, we pay attention to many more details. We become open to the beauty, newness, and sacredness that each moment can provide. We can focus more on the goodness that derives from helping vulnerable patients in their time of deepest need.

As we explored earlier, we can spend time diagnosing what is right.

We can also get back in touch with the world that is right in front of us.

Stepping Out of Autopilot

So many times, our lives feel like a blur. We go through our days skimming the surface, not fully experiencing the moments we're in. We look back over the day and we're not sure what we had for lunch, or if we even had lunch. We come to the end of a week and can't recall what each day brought. In the midst of thousands of thoughts, we miss what was right in front of us the whole time.

Time goes by. Our kids grow up. Our relationships shift and change. Loved ones age and die. We wonder where the years went, out of touch with what is actually going on in the moments of our lives.

Living on autopilot takes many forms. We drive from point A to point B and don't know how we got there. We eat meals, often delicious ones, and barely notice the texture and taste on our tongue and lips. We find ourselves saying things we later regret, not having fully thought them out beforehand—almost as if we have no control over what comes out of our mouths.

Another word for autopilot is *mindlessness*.

Instead of paying attention to the moments that make up our lives, we're missing them. Instead of deciding where we focus, we're letting our minds flit here and there, without taking in what's actually in front of us. Instead of being intentional regarding what's important to us, we're meandering along, putting our energy into whatever it is that arises in our minds over the course of a busy day.

We're letting life run us instead of being the ones running our lives.

Brian had developed a pattern of autopilot regarding his interactions with nurses and patients. As part of this autopilot, he was not fully aware of his own behavior and words. He was definitely not aware of their impact.

With the shift to mindfulness, we see our automatic patterns more clearly. Once we spot (read: diagnose) them, we can question whether they are serving us or not.

Being Versus Doing

It's said that instead of human beings, we should be called "human doings." Particularly for physicians, what we learn is to do, do, do. We don't typically learn to stop, pause, and reflect—or to just be. Instead, all the swirling of thoughts keeps us perpetually reacting to everything around us.

That is the nature of thought.

In effect, all this doing keeps us from just being in the moment.

Mark Williams, an Oxford professor of psychology, describes how our minds are experts at doing—not just the physical doing of moving, driving, and so on, but mental doing as well. In many ways, our minds are busy as a sort of discrepancy monitor, trying to figure things out, solving, and comparing whatever is happening to what has previously been seen.[6]

Unfortunately, all this mental activity makes it difficult for us to rest. Busy, busy, busy, the overactive mind keeps us in constant motion, away from the moments that are happening right now.

In being mode, however, we are actually *in* the moments of our lives. Our senses are alive; we're aware of the information they're bringing—outside of our mind's interpretation of our experience—and we're actually immersed in the experience itself.

Instead of adding an overlay of judgment, comparison, and interpretation, when we are being, rather than mentally doing, we are taking in reality firsthand. Doing so, we see that our thoughts are simply thoughts, not facts. As we have seen, they are transient mental events that arise, pass through our minds, and dissipate; real for only as long as they are present—in actuality, a fleeting moment in time.

When we're in the autopilot of doing, we don't always make this distinction—yet we can. For busy, overburdened physicians, this is critically important.

Tyrone, a 55-year-old academic internist, was having difficulty keeping up with his practice. Perpetually behind on charts, he typically ran late for each patient. He'd start his day thinking it would go better and then find himself behind once again. When this occurred, he'd get anxious and try to do more of the multitasking he had perfected in his training. *Maybe if I just do more in the same time*, he thought, *I'll finally be able to catch up.*

But not only did Tyrone not catch up, he was increasingly exhausted trying to stay on top of it all.

Tyrone shared an important realization: "When I trained for triathlons in college, Gail, there were many points where I stopped and rested so I could get to the finish. But now that I'm in this busy practice, it's as if I'm constantly running. I'm never stopping to recharge."

And how long can we run without recharging and filling our tank?

As you likely know, we can only run so long on empty. For some reason, many physicians think we can do this long term, yet, when we do, it almost always comes back to bite us, typically in the form of burnout.

Learning to Fill Our Tanks

Physicians tell me all the time that they don't have time to exercise, make or procure nutritious meals, or get enough sleep. We learn in our training that we are invulnerable, the one in charge, always the captain of the team. While we are immersed in the abject vulnerability of our patients' physical bodies, training doesn't teach us that *our* bodies require the same care. We don't learn to pause and make sure we have what we need to run the next leg of our journey.

Even physicians can run on empty for only so long.

To help busy physicians nourish themselves, I advise what I call "The Daily Dose of Goodness." By this I mean one small thing they can commit to every single day that is just for them—something to nourish themselves and fill their tank.

It can be something very small: A healthy(ish) treat, a walk down the hall, meditating for 5 minutes, listening to enjoyable music, a cup of soothing tea, or a meaningful moment with family or friends. The list of options is endless; it is whatever that physician finds positive, nourishing, and sustaining.

You may read this and wonder how you can make this kind of time when *I'm barely keeping up with my inbox.*

Here's what I'll counter with—what is the cost of not doing so? What is the cost of treating life like a sprint, not a marathon—or even like a calm walk—to be experienced and enjoyed at a natural pace?

The answer lies in noticing the ways running on empty keeps you trapped in burnout. In addition to all the mental busyness, there is often a storyline that there isn't enough time. Of course, time is the precious commodity that we all want more of. Yet, perhaps there is actually more time in our days than we realize, and taking 5 or 10 minutes for a dose of nurturance often goes a long way.

When we step out of autopilot and slow all the mental doing, we experience a sense of greater spaciousness. When we take the time to pause and move into inhabiting the moments of our days, we find that we have more time, not less.

Tyrone began to take such pauses. He shared, "When I pause and slow myself down, I realize that I actually have more time."

The old adage is true—the tortoise beats the hare.

Thoughts and Burnout

Amidst the difficult and busy life the modern physician leads, the torrent of thoughts that travel through our minds each day saps the little energy we have after meeting the many demands of our work. The annoying roommate, who's quite comfortable living rent-free in the space between our ears, has been jabbering away all day, commenting on all the shortcomings and saying next to nothing about all that has gone well.

Fortunately for us, our roommate is a guest we can detach from in our day-to-day realities. We can become empowered to decide which of the roommate monologues we tune in to. We can recognize how the stories this roommate has spun about our lives have contributed to our burnout (something we'll touch on in the next chapter), and we can let these stories go. We can also notice when it's taking us away from the moments of our lives and come back to the present. These moments help give us energy and remind us why we became physicians in the first place.

Mindfulness helps us recognize when the roommate is yapping away and affords us the autonomy to ignore the inner discourse that only serves to increase our distress.

For those of you who still aren't sure about this whole mindfulness thing, let me be clear: Mindfulness cannot reverse the many changes that have occurred in healthcare, create resources to ensure our patients can afford their medications, eradicate the electronic record, or change the fact that the digital age means an almost constant filling of our inbox. The corporatization of healthcare is all too real, and the emphasis on productivity and the bottom line is here to stay. Physicians no longer reside at the apex, and that is not exactly an easy pill to swallow.

I hate to say it, but none of this appears to be going away anytime soon. I wish this were not the case, but it is. And I, like you, applaud *any* effort that can be made to rectify the all-too-numerous maladies of our healthcare systems.

At the same time, what mindfulness *can do* is help us develop mastery over our minds. Mindfulness helps us gain agency over what we think, feel, and do. For those of us struggling with the ways control in healthcare has been wrested from us, this agency (read: autonomy) is critically important. While we have limited control over the many external shifts, we have the potential for complete control over ourselves.

At the end of the day, mindfulness takes our more than 20,000 random daily thoughts and helps us make sense of them, deciding which ones we want to believe and which we don't. It is what allows us to see when our thoughts have swept us away from the reality right in front of us.

It is this autonomy over our own thoughts and minds that mindfulness provides. It is this autonomy that is at the core of a *Mindful MD*, that makes the difference between burnout and a career and life of meaning, purpose, and fulfillment.

MINDFULNESS EXERCISE: OPEN SKY MEDITATION

One way to recognize that you are not your thoughts is building the ability to see your thoughts for exactly what they are. Picturing the mind as the open sky can help you do so.

Sit quietly and let your eyes gently close. Bring your attention to your breathing, not making it anything special, just connecting with it. Notice the rise and fall of your chest. See if you can keep your focus on this movement, paying attention to how it feels inside you. Try to follow one entire breath from beginning to end, focusing purely on your physical sensations.

Now imagine that your mind is like the sky—vast and spacious, without beginning or end. It's a sunny day, and your sky is majestic and bright. When a thought or an emotion comes into your mind, imagine that it's a cloud in your blue sky, gently passing by. See it arise, move across, and fade away. Easily and naturally, the thought passes through your mind.

Just like the sky, your mind is undisturbed by the clouds that inhabit it, remaining open, calm, and expansive.

Just as clouds are a natural part of the sky, so are your thoughts. There's nothing wrong with your mind for producing thoughts. See if you can let the thoughts pass through, gently and without duress. Don't judge yourself for having thoughts; we all do.

When you notice that a thought is present, gently bring your attention back to your breath. Sometimes this will be easier than at other times, as now and then your thoughts may be like storm clouds. That's okay too. Simply notice this and see if you can let the stormy thoughts and feelings that arise pass by without getting swept away by them.

Every time you notice a thought or an emotion, that's a moment of mindfulness. That's what meditation is all about.

Sit this way for 10 minutes, then gently open your eyes.

As you go through your day, see if you can imagine your thoughts in just this same way, arising and passing by without disrupting the calm of your mind. See if you can recognize the mental chatter as the annoying room-mate that it is.

After all, you are not your thoughts. The narrator isn't you.

Q AND A

1. I've tried to meditate, but I can't. What if my mind is just too busy?

Yes, the human mind is quite a busy place, isn't it?

With meditation, we're not trying to turn off thoughts. We wouldn't be able to even if we tried since the job of our mind is to produce thoughts. Rather, we're training our mind to direct attention to where we want our attention directed. We're getting curious about our inner world, paying attention to what's going on. Each time we realize we're having a thought is actually a moment of mindfulness. It means we're paying attention; we're seeing what is going on. That's the time to gently shift our attention away from the thought and back to the anchor point of our breathing. That's all we're doing. Over and over and over.

For most of us, because our minds are such busy places, meditation requires a lot of practice. In fact, that is exactly why it's called a practice!

2. You say that thoughts are simply transient mental events that pass through like clouds. But I find myself having the same thought over and over, and I can't seem to turn this off. What can I do when my thoughts don't pass through the way you're describing?

You're describing something that many can relate to. We have a thought and our mind repeats it over and over, almost as if it's stuck in a groove and can't figure out how to move on. This type of rumination can be quite frustrating, can't it?

It turns out that some thoughts are sticky, like that flypaper I mentioned, and our mind sees them as important and keeps pulling our attention toward them.

What's key is building awareness of this pattern. You can even call out when your mind does this with something like, "There goes my mind repeating that thought again." While this may sound a bit foolish, it can help build your sense of choice as to how much attention you give the thought. It will take time and practice, but you'll find yourself ruminating less over time.

3. How do I know when my thoughts are me or when they are the annoying roommate you describe?

For most of us, our inner narrator is speaking to us throughout our days, so much so that it can be difficult to separate ourselves from its incessant dialogue. It takes practice to distinguish our voice from all that noisy discourse.

Sitting quietly in meditation is a key way of building this skill. You'll learn more about meditation when you become the observer (part of our third way), but, for now, I encourage you to start doing the open sky meditation exercise. You'll rapidly see the transient and insubstantial nature of your thoughts more clearly. You'll be creating that all-important gap, and that, too, will help you see just how many of your thoughts are the roommate and not you.

2. Step Out of Mental Stories

"The real voyage of discovery consists not in seeking new landscapes, but in having new eyes."
—Marcel Proust

Boring. Tedious. Meaningless.
Those were the words that repeated in Dianna's mind.

Boring. Tedious. Meaningless.

Over and over and over again.

Dianna had lost her spark.

Dianna was a 39-year-old endocrinologist who had been drawn to her specialty for the combination of science and caring it afforded. Dianna's office wall boasted the pedigree of diplomas many would envy: A prestigious medical school, board certification in internal medicine and endocrinology, and top-name hospitals for residency and fellowship.

Now, eight years into her practice, she felt frustrated and exhausted, like "a meaningless hamster spinning on a meaningless wheel." The science that so fascinated her wasn't what mattered for patients who cheated on their diabetic diets, were noncompliant with their insulin, or gained 20 pounds instead of achieving the weight loss she had prescribed. She was bored with the mild thyroid problems, osteoporosis, and seemingly endless diabetes and obesity that filled her days. She felt a sense of meaninglessness and inadequacy. She had gone into medicine to cure disease, after all, and it was challenging to her when she could not.

When I asked her to write down what went through her mind as she saw her patients, she presented me with a list:

- *No one listens to my instructions.*
- *Nothing I do matters.*
- *This is not why I went to medical school.*
- *It's all a waste of my time.*

Dianna's mind broadcast these thoughts throughout the day. The story was building upon itself and unconsciously trapping her in a negative way of viewing her patients. It was a way that was neither satisfying for them nor for her. This mental story sucked the purpose out of her days and became a self-fulfilling prophecy—her patient visits *became* boring, tedious, and seemingly meaningless.

Dianna's workdays were long and exhausting. When she finally got home to her family at the end of a busy day, this story kept playing, over and over, her mind stuck in mental overdrive. *Another miserable day spinning on the wheel. It is all humdrum and dull. I can't stand it.*

She needed rest and reprieve from all the demands, yet her mind was busy telling her about all the problems in her day, and little about any of the positives. Who wouldn't be exhausted?

I spent time validating her struggle. It is painful to go through all the demands of medical school and residency only to find yourself unfulfilled on the other side. Having toiled countless hours, devoted yourself to helping others, and delayed significant gratification, it can be demoralizing to feel as though your work is for naught.

Dianna's story was that her work was completely meaningless. Like the stories that most of us tell ourselves, it was completely black or white. Dianna's story minimized any positive impact that she was having. It took a bit of coaching for her to get back in touch with that side of her work.

I asked her to tell me about things that were going well.

After some significant racking of her brain, she finally told me about a diabetic patient who, despite taking her insulin as prescribed, was frustrated about her high blood sugars and had become tearful as she told Dianna how hopeless she felt about her condition. Seeing the patient's distress, Dianna had pushed herself to quiet her mind and focus on this vulnerable person who so needed her help. She listened intently and acknowledged the patient's sadness and fear, and went out of her way to be present and do what she could to figure out the best plan forward. She made time to answer questions and connected in a way that helped the patient feel understood and seen.

As Dianna walked from the exam room back to her office, she felt moved by the meeting. *I wish I could have utilized all my scientific training,* she thought, *but I know that just being there for this patient was the best intervention I could provide. Maybe she'll make the changes, maybe she won't, but at least I showed up in a way that I feel proud of.*

As Dianna shared this with me, her shoulders dropped and there was a softening in her face. It was clearly deeply meaningful for her to connect with this patient and do what she could to allay her concerns. While not every interaction would provide this fulfillment, when Dianna focused more on the meaningful ones and less on the negative mental story, she was able to take in the sustenance she needed to get through the inevitable mundane aspects of her work.

I asked her to tell me about other patients she had helped. After sharing a few other experiences where she connected well with the patient, the shift in Dianna's demeanor was palpable. There was a sense of aliveness, previously hidden. Without a doubt, this shift took her to a place of greater engagement, as well as a place of greater satisfaction with being a physician. "Maybe things aren't as bad as I've thought," she said. "Maybe I *can* find a way to stay engaged in this work, after all."

Dianna's mind had been so busy telling her a story about what a waste of time these visits were that she couldn't take in the fulfillment the interactions provided. Many of her patient visits did follow a similar script, and many patients did fail to heed her recommendations. But the constant story of 100 percent failure wasn't inspiring or accurate, and stepping out of it allowed Dianna to completely refresh her perspective about her work.

Stepping out of the stories our minds are so adept at creating is the second way mindfulness restores your autonomy and cures healthcare burnout.

After all, these stories are being told in the closed space that lies between the two human ears. Unseen by others, and rarely brought into the light of day, our mental stories are typically unexamined and unchallenged. They run in the background, out of conscious awareness, yet they color almost everything about our experience.

The stories the physician's mind spins are not just centered around the routine, sometimes repetitive, parts of practice. They are often about fear, worry, and even catastrophe.

This was the case for Moses, a successful cardiology department chair, who came to coaching overwhelmed by anxiety. Early in our work, he confided in me that he ruminated about almost every decision he made and was up many nights worrying about what might occur with his patients.

- *What if I missed something important in that young man with palpitations?*
- *I'm not sure I ordered the right test for that elderly woman with congestive heart failure.*
- *If I screw up with a patient, I'll be facing a malpractice suit—I just know it.*

Moses's catastrophic stories were not just about patients. Whether it was regarding department finances or the actions of his teenage daughter, his mind often went to the worst-case scenario. Interestingly, however, he didn't connect his worst-case thinking to his anxiety.

This highly intellectual leader had not seen that his anxiety was being fueled by his mind's proclivity for worst-case thinking.

As if this wasn't surprising enough, when I asked Moses to look back over his career and tell me how often the worst case had occurred, his response really took the cake: "I've been in my role for the last five years, and it has actually never happened, even though I have almost constantly worried that it would." He broke out in laughter, now able to see the absurdity of the story lines his mind had made up.

Seeing the powerful impact his own thought processes had over his state, he exclaimed: "It's like a drug with a terrible side effect profile. This is definitely one we need to take off the formulary!"

Stories and Suffering

While Dianna's and Moses's stories may sound extreme, it is not just the doctor who has stories that color their experience. Nurses have stories. Patients, too, have stories about doctors, the healthcare system, and their illness.

In my years as a physician in hospice, caring for patients struck down by the tragedy of an incurable illness, my patients had mental stories aplenty about their lives and illnesses. Many of these were about unfairness, denial, and even shame. I saw patients denying their inevitable passing, which ironically prevented them from passing on their own terms. These stories kept my patients from having time with loved ones, getting relief from their pain, and spending their final hours surrounded by family in the comfort of their own home (many spent them in the ICU hooked up to machines). It was difficult seeing patients die in this way, knowing that while their death could not be prevented, much of their suffering could be. What I saw was how the stories created by their minds served to keep them from finding healing and closure with those most important in their lives—their children, their spouses, and others.

In my decade coaching physicians, I've heard innumerable stories, many involving a sense of being a disappointment or an imposter:

- Lev, a 49-year-old hospitalist: *I'm not as smart as other doctors. I feel like a complete fraud.*
- Wendy, a 34-year-old obstetrics and gynecology resident: *They only let me into med school because there was a quota from rural areas in my state. I've never belonged.*
- Peter, a 53-year-old dermatologist: *I don't have the expanse of knowledge others have. I feel like I'm a fake dermatologist.*
- Avani, a 58-year-old anesthesiologist at an elite academic medical center: *I'm embarrassed that I haven't had even one article published in a major medical journal.*
- Alison, a 62-year-old family physician: *A good physician only recommends things like exercise and meditation if they are actually doing it themselves, and I'm definitely not meeting that bar.*
- Jim, a 53-year-old allergist: *We don't have the same kind of house other physicians have. There's stuff everywhere, and we've never had the money for that kitchen remodel I hear my colleagues talking about. I'm a disappointment to my profession, and to my wife and family.*

Each of these physicians had a mental story of inadequacy. The culmination of distorted thoughts, the stories focused on a sense of deficit and left the physicians isolated, anguished, and depleted. There was no objective evidence that they were a disappointment or an imposter, just a mental story. Yet, it was one that took them to a self-constructed world of judgment and comparison, away from the good they were doing caring for sick patients each and every day. And, like Dianna, when the story was repeated enough times in their minds, it began to feel like an irrefutable truth.

Difficult enough to face the demands of a physician's work. Overwhelming with the overlay of the mental story.

A key aspect of mindfulness is realizing that our stories can cause more suffering than the actual difficulties we face.

While physicians are just as likely as the general population to generate these mental myths, in my experience, we are far more likely to be stuck believing them. Because of the fixed medical mindset training fosters—along with the constant need to be "right" that we were taught—we have a harder time than most realizing that many of the stories we tell ourselves couldn't be further from the truth.

For a profession that prides itself on following facts, evidence, and the scientific method, however, it is almost astonishing how much stock we physicians put into the rather subjective stories of our minds.

To unravel the patterns that have kept us mired in burnout, we have to bring this mental world out of the closed space inside the cranium and into the light of day. Doing so requires becoming acutely aware of just what our minds are up to. With mindful awareness, we see that the human mind is a master storyteller, spinning stories about who we are, what we do, and the world and people around us. This is the mental training that mindfulness provides. With this training, we become the master of our minds, deciding which stories we want to believe and which we don't.

Once we grasp these important truths, we can step out of the story and simply observe the telling of it. We become the witness of the story, rather than its hostage.

Pain Versus Suffering: A Tale of Two Arrows

As you read this, you're likely wondering how to manage your mind's storytelling tendency. This is not by banishing the stories. If you try this, you'll likely experience a great deal of frustration, finding that the stories have that sticky flypaper tendency mentioned earlier.

Notably, Carl Jung, one of the most influential psychiatrists of all time, contended that "what you resist not only persists, but will grow in size,"[1] which is often shortened to the pithy adage "what you resist, persists."

It turns out that the more we push something away, the more our minds tend to react by holding on to it. Conversely, when we accept reality as it truly is and view our stories as nothing more than a story, we can watch them fade away.

Moreover, as we begin to see our stories for exactly what they are, they rapidly lose their power. It's as if the wind has been taken from their sails.

We can facilitate this process with something called "the two arrows of pain and suffering."

Let's face it: Pain is part of life. None of us get through life without some measure of pain—physical or emotional, minor or intense. The concept of the two arrows helps us see, however, that for every difficulty we face, there is primary and second-ary pain. There is the pain of the difficulty itself: A diagnosis of cancer, problems with your kids, being trained as a specialist yet seeing patients who don't involve your level of expertise, a chal-lenging boss, accidents, job instability—difficulties of all sorts.

We'll call these the first arrows.

In addition to the pain caused by these first arrows, there is also the pain and suffering created by the stories our minds are so expert at creating. These are what we'll call the second arrows. And guess where these second arrows are pointed? They are typically pointed directly at ourselves.

To exemplify this: Pain is tripping on your kid's toy train so your cup of coffee is flung onto the new white carpet. Suffering is spending the rest of the day telling yourself what a fool you are for stopping at Starbucks and for choosing white!

To better understand the concept of the two arrows, let's look at Isaiah, a 52-year-old emergency physician.

Isaiah was an excellent physician, well respected by the physicians and nurses he had worked with for years. He was the one who could be counted on to rapidly diagnose the prob-lem a patient had and just as rapidly put the needed treatment plan in place.

Isaiah was on duty late one night when a patient came in with abdominal pain. It was a busy shift, with a waiting room full of sick patients, an understaffing of nurses, and the physician assis-tant who typically took the less serious cases out sick.

Isaiah was stretched thin.

This particular case was challenging, as the patient's pain was out of proportion to what the tests were showing. Isaiah had ordered a CT scan just to be sure.

Unfortunately, the radiologist on call missed a critical finding, leading to a delay in diagnosis and to the patient needing additional surgery. Although the patient was fine in the end, he had seen all those billboards sponsored by "ambulance-chasing attorneys" and filed a lawsuit. While Isaiah had done nothing wrong, the patient's attorney pointed fingers not just at the radiologist, but also the doctor who had ordered the CT. Isaiah happened to be that doctor.

Having a lawsuit filed against you is devastating, one of the worst fears a physician has, and something no physician wants to experience. That is the first arrow.

Of course, fear, worry, and anxiety are part of this experience. Without a doubt, a physician's career brings many difficult events, from having to tell a patient of a new diagnosis of cancer, to trying to keep up with all the latest advances in a complex specialized field, to the shift from the autonomy of private practice to being an employee in a corporate system. We might call these occupational hazards of the job, and physicians typically have limited control over many of them.

The second arrow, however, is where the mind takes the basic facts of the situation—the first arrow—and spins a story, often magnifying our distress with an overlay of fear, anger, worry, anxiety, or shame. The second arrow takes the form of self-blame, comparisons, accusations, and predictions of a worst-case future.

For Isaiah, the second arrows were many.

Isaiah imagined himself on the witness stand, facing question after question, humiliated by a punishing plaintiff's attorney. He imagined massive legal fees, missed tuition payments, and an imminent foreclosure. He imagined his face on the front page of his local newspaper with a headline proclaiming him a rogue, a deviant, a physician to stay away from at all costs. He imagined being shamed by his colleagues and cast out from the profession.

Isaiah's mind went into overdrive, producing second arrow upon second arrow. He was up many nights imagining all these bad events, playing them over and over in his mind, and worrying about what might occur. He had a gnawing sense in his abdomen and found it hard to relax with his wife and daughters. He was so on edge that he even started yelling at the new puppy every time she whined to go out for a walk.

But had Isaiah actually been on the witness stand? Had he paid those legal fees? Had his mortgage been foreclosed? Had his face actually appeared in the paper? No!

In reality, none of these things had occurred. But Isaiah's mind created these second arrows, pointed at no one but himself, creating a great deal of stress, worry, and fear. The second arrows took Isaiah well beyond the facts of the matter into the land of fear, worry, rumination, shame, gnawing abdominal discomfort, irritability, and sleepless nights.

As the infamous Mark Twain saying goes, "I have been through some terrible things in my life, most of which never happened."

This is where mindfulness comes in.

We cannot control many of the first arrows life sends our way. We can, however, pay attention to what our minds are up to and learn strategies to decrease the sting of the second arrows. After all, they are based on our minds' capacity to generate stories of fear and woe, and not on reality.

Few of us are immune, and I'll pause here to confess to a story I told myself for years, full of second arrows of my own.

When my son, Daavi, was 17, he became quite ill with severe fatigue and abdominal pain; he would come home from school and lie, groaning in pain, on the couch. Almost overnight, he went from star student to barely getting his homework done.

At first, the pediatrician thought he was faking his symptoms. Then she diagnosed him with constipation. Eventually, after a hospital stay and scoping of both his upper and lower intestines, the diagnosis of Crohn's disease was made.

As a physician, the negative, problem-focused lens filled me with memories of bad cases I'd seen. The 25-year-old with Crohn's who, after a series of surgeries for strictures, was left with only a tube for feeding. The 48-year-old with Crohn's who came in septic and was resistant to almost every antibiotic we tried.

It was a stormy time, but once the diagnosis was made, Daavi was put on medication that, in the near decade since, has successfully controlled his condition. Besides having to stay away from gluten, he's a completely strapping and healthy young man.

But many times since, I've told myself the doomsday story that I caused his illness. That I hadn't cooked him the right foods and hadn't fed him enough fresh vegetables. That I had been so busy with my career that I hadn't paid enough attention to his needs. That I had been egregiously selfish and way too career-focused. That any other physician parent would have known better. That I had completely failed as a mother.

All this time, Daavi was the one who was suffering. It was he who was on the couch, he who had the abdominal pain, and he who needed his mother to be fully focused on helping him cope and manage this difficult disease. Yet, my mind was often off on this story of blame, with second arrows about me and not about him at all. Perhaps the stories kept my mind locked into an effort to control something that, in reality, I could not. But *ouch*, those second arrows went straight into my maternal heart.

Reading this, you can likely see that one of the interesting things about second arrows is that a story that plagues us for what feels like a lifetime often appears completely ridiculous to others. Just as my story that I caused my son's chronic illness by not providing nightly home-cooked meals likely sounds like complete nonsense to others, it's a story that I repeated to myself over and over again.

Indeed, our second arrows can be far removed from reality—that's exactly why it is so important to see them for what they truly are.

Lest you think this is something unique to physicians and moms, let me be clear: Second arrows occur for everyone. As we've discussed, the human mind has a phenomenal ability to tell stories, spinning yarn upon yarn, generating fear, worry, and stress seemingly at every turn.

Our minds are experts at taking us on all kinds of second-arrow journeys.

But nowhere are these second arrows more costly than in healthcare, where we are in the business of relieving suffering. Yet these arrows are only creating our own suffering and eroding our ability to truly be present—for our patients, our loved ones, and ourselves.

Understanding this concept of the two arrows is critical to unlocking the fixed medical mindset and the anguish it generates. It is also critical to reducing the overwhelm that a career in healthcare can evoke.

Mindfulness provides the pathway for reducing the extra layer of suffering the second arrows create. When we can see what our minds are up to, we realize there is an out. We don't have to believe all the stories our mind is producing. Perhaps we have a choice in whether we believe the second arrows or not. Perhaps we can learn to let go.

Letting Go of the Story, Finding the Truth

Returning to my maternal true confession, you were likely finding it easy to spot my story of self-criticism, self-blame, and parental neglect. You could probably also see that I did not cause my son's Crohn's disease. Yet, my mind visited this story frequently over quite a number of years. As you can imagine, it was not a story that left me feeling good about myself. No, it left me depleted, down on myself, and full of guilt. It was based on no objective evidence, yet I didn't stop to question its veracity. For a long time, I wasn't even aware that the story was there.

However, we can become aware of the stories we tell ourselves, learn to question them, and let go of the ones that are falsehoods and are only serving to increase our misery. With mindfulness, we develop our ability to observe and investigate our stories, and then separate from the ones that don't hold the truth of our experience. When we do, we can free ourselves from the pain they cause us to experience. We can live more authentically and with greater presence with those around us, be they our patients, our children, or anyone else.

Psychiatrist and neuroscientist Judson Brewer did just that. In his 2021 book *Unwinding Anxiety*, he discusses his own experience utilizing mindfulness to stem mental stories. He shares how during his psychiatry residency, he began to experience panic attacks. He had all the telltale signs—rapid heart rate, shallow breathing, and a sense of things closing in on him. Additionally, he noticed that his mind produced stories (read: second arrows) about the panic attacks. *Oh no, I had a panic attack; this is bad. What if I have another one? How will this impact my ability to take care of patients?*

As challenging as it was to experience panic attacks, worse still was this story of worry, fear, and anxiety his mind spun. Because he'd been meditating for some time, though, he could see the story and simply explain to himself that he was experiencing panic, without adding the overlay of second arrows. Instead of getting swept away by a story that only served to worsen his already difficult state, he could simply observe the experience.[2]

As Dr. Brewer's experience indicates, simply noticing we're off in a story is often enough to break its spell. That is the power of mindful awareness.

You may be wondering how you can do this yourself.

Here are the steps I used with my second arrows:

Distinguish between the first and second arrows.

What is fact and what is fiction? The first arrow was that Daavi developed Crohn's disease. That was a fact. But the "I caused my son's Crohn's" story was the second arrow my mind took me to, playing in the background of my mind so frequently that I initially didn't even notice it was there. Once I could spot the playing and replaying, however, I could begin separating myself from the story. I could create that all-important gap between my mental dialogue and myself.

Determine whether the second arrow is 100 percent true.

Oftentimes, there may be a kernel of truth that spirals into a full-blown case-closed scenario in our minds. Yes, diet can play a role in causing Crohn's disease. But alongside genetic predisposition, Daavi's age, his gender, and a multitude of other factors, it was low on the list.

The stories we cast often fail to acknowledge this kind of countervailing information. There were plenty of things I did as a parent that contributed to my son's well-being and health—but the story that played over and over again was that I was a terrible mother who hadn't served him enough broccoli.

One of the keys to unwinding a second-arrow story we've gotten caught in is looking at it under a microscope like this. Can we believe it with 100 percent certainty? Can we identify counter information?

Allow the second arrows to pass by without giving them undue attention.

Once I saw just how often this inaccurate narrative was entering my thoughts, I could consciously allow it to simply pass through my mind.

The key to getting over this mental hang-up was letting go of the shame, emotion, and power of the story and just accepting it for the story it was. Once I was able to notice the thought pattern (read: story) coming up—without reacting, getting sucked into an argument with it (which you can never win), or feeling any shame for the story popping up—it passed through remarkably quickly.

The combination of bringing the stories into mindful awareness, questioning their veracity, and letting them pass through without getting hooked by them encompasses the key skills that help us detach from the storytelling mind. This involves becoming the observer of our mind, which we'll cover more in depth in our third way.

We are applying mindful awareness not as a vague, faraway concept, but as the pragmatic exercising of moment-by-moment awareness of exactly what our minds are up to. Doing so takes us out of the storytelling and brings us into the reality of our lives.

Utilizing mindfulness in this way is a powerful antidote to burnout—one that gives *Mindful MDs* true autonomy over our own minds and the stories that only serve to multiply the difficulties we're facing in our lives and careers.

MINDFULNESS EXERCISE: WORKING WITH THE SECOND ARROW OF PAIN AND SUFFERING

Life involves pain: This is the truth of human existence for all of us. In addition to the painful events we experience, however, we've seen how the mind tells stories that create more suffering than the painful events themselves.

Right now, bring to mind any difficulty you are experiencing in your life or work. It may be anything from an illness to a difficult boss to a financial challenge. That difficulty is the first arrow. Write that down here (or on a separate piece of paper).

The first arrow is _____

_____

Now, bring to mind your thoughts and stories about this difficulty. These are the second arrows.

Write down as many of these as you can.

The second arrows are _____

_____

_____

_____

_____

Now ask yourself:

Is my second arrow 100 percent true? Is there any counter information?

Take a moment now to notice how you feel when you experience the second arrows. Do you feel calm and content? Or sad, fearful, and anxious? Do the second arrows increase or decrease the suffering you're experiencing from the first-arrow difficulty?

If you noticed that your level of suffering increased, what can you say to yourself to quiet the second arrows? For example, you might say, "It's okay. None of those bad things have actually happened." Or, "We're going to get through this. We've gotten through difficult times before."

Take a moment to write down what you can say to yourself.

I hope you'll utilize this exercise multiple times and in a variety of circumstances. It will help you build your mindfulness muscle and avoid a lot of unnecessary suffering.

Q AND A

1. You divide the first and second arrows, but they all seem the same to me. How do I start distinguishing them?

I understand that this can be confusing. The first arrow is the fact of the matter—what actually happened. That could be an illness, a divorce, or a challenging conversation with your boss, spouse, teen, or patient. As these are the facts, they are typically unchangeable and beyond your control.

The second arrow, in contradistinction, is the story your mind generates about the facts. For example, you might think: *This is bad. Why does this keep happening to me? I never should have* ___. The second arrows are not factual. They are simply stories and not reality.

I encourage you to utilize the two-arrows exercise, as you'll begin to see the distinction more clearly. Don't just utilize it once. Since our minds are so good at generating fiction, it takes practice to see the second arrows more clearly.

2. You say that feeling like an imposter is just a mental story. But what if I truly am an imposter?

Your question affirms just how good our minds are at creating stories that seduce us into believing them. The story about being an imposter is an extremely common one, for physicians and many others. We bring mindfulness to this by questioning what the evidence is. Is there anything objective or is it largely a subjective sense? With my son's illness, my mind grabbed onto a story that had absolutely no objective basis. I had to step out of my autopilot belief in the story and step into mindful questioning of its veracity. Similarly, I have helped hundreds of physicians see that their sense of being an imposter is simply a mental fiction, without any objective data to support it.

The suffering caused by imposter stories can be profound. In fact, I have developed a self-paced online course* that utilizes mindfulness and other strategies to help vanquish the imposter phenomenon. Any of us can overcome the persnickety sense of being an imposter.

3. Like Dianna, I find my work tedious and boring, but this isn't a story my mind made up; it's the truth. What should I do?

I'm wondering how you know this is the truth. What's the evidence? Is it possible that "tedious and boring" is simply a story your mind has created? In other words, if you spend time working with the two arrows, you'll start seeing just how seductive the mental stories are.

Further, you can challenge yourself to try out a new story. When Dianna shifted to curiosity about her patients (and her stories), she found herself less focused on "tedious and boring" and more focused on the patient and their illness. She was moving from being the captive to the master of her mind.

At the same time, while your work may be boring in some ways, replaying the mental story of boredom likely isn't helping make it more interesting, is it?

In truth, we all have a choice in how we view ourselves, others, and the circumstances of our lives. That is the autonomy we each can have.

---

* - https://gailgazelle.com/imposter-no-more-course/

3. REDUCE REACTIVITY

"You are the sky. Everything else is just the weather."
—Pema Chodron

Rereading the email from his practice manager a third time, Anil was still annoyed. And angry. *How can this be happening?* he nearly uttered out loud.

The emails had become a regular part of his week, arriving in his inbox and indicating that his charts were overdue. As per usual, these "nastygrams" came complete with a ranking of where he stood relative to the other physicians in his group. Here he was again, at the bottom of everyone in his department.

A mid-career family physician, his passion was taking care of patients, and he had picked his specialty for the diverse population it allowed him to care for. Moving from performing a dementia screening on an 85-year-old great-grandmother to telling jokes to a 5-year-old to distract them from their vaccine shot was exactly what he loved.

What he didn't love, however, was all the time it took to get the notes documenting their visits done. In fact, he rarely got his notes done during the workday, and his charts typically spilled over to weeknights and weekends. While his wife and 10-year-old daughter were out bike riding or watching *American Idol,* Anil sat in isolation staring at the computer screen.

He was constantly playing catch-up. As is the case for many physicians, Anil felt trapped by the demands of the electronic medical record. What's more, he was being *sent* for coaching. Having never gotten below an A– in high school and college, he felt like this was a big fat F.

In our first coaching session, Anil told me just how discouraging this was for him.

He looked haggard and kept his head down, with an almost morose affect as he told me about his plight. His physical demeanor mirrored the lack of vitality and hope he was living.

To say that Anil was burned out would be putting it mildly.

The work began with the *Mindful MD* chart audit.™ In addition to the number of clicks, hacks, and shortcuts many physicians learn, we have to get at what often lies beneath and keeps the physician stuck, and this audit helps get at the patterns that are doing so. To this end, we needed to explore the emotions he experienced around charting. I suspected there were many.

Anil shared that when he sat down to chart, or even when he contemplated getting his charts done, he felt angry that this is what his life as a physician had become. Shaking his head in dismay, he said, "This is not why I went into medicine, Gail! I went into medicine to help people, not to sit at a damn computer. Sometimes I get so angry it feels like my head is going to explode."

"This is definitely not why you went into medicine, Anil," I reassured him, "and I have coached many physicians who have expressed the exact same thing. It's perfectly normal to have these emotions around charting, but it sure sounds intense for you."

Anil's shoulders dropped, heartened to receive affirmation of his experience. His mind had been off in negative self-judgment, not just about his difficulty succeeding at charting but also accusing him of being a procrastinator. Not to mention being soft or unfit regarding the swirl of emotions he was experiencing. Insult upon injury—it was a lot to bear.

Next I asked, "What do you do to manage this intensity?"

He looked surprised by this question. After a long pause, he said, "What *can* I do? I mainly just sit there and stew. It's weird, but sometimes I almost zone out. I have no idea what's going on, but then the time just passes, and I still have dozens of charts in the queue. This has got to stop! If it continues, my job may be on the line."

Reading this, you can see how trapped Anil was by charting and by the emotions charting generated within him.

In the previous two chapters, we examined our thoughts—randomly generated transient mental blips that can sap our energy and confidence—and our stories—the culmination of these thoughts. We also explored how you can choose not to identify with these.

We'll now look at the third way mindfulness restores your autonomy and cures burnout—by reducing reactivity. We'll examine patterns—the day-to-day sticking points that we continually run into—and you'll learn how mindfulness is just the medicine needed to move away from these traps as well.

Charting Our Emotional Storms

In many ways, what Anil was experiencing was a recurring emotional storm. On top of the stress of getting his charts done, he was overloaded with emotion.

Of course, we humans are emotional creatures—this is part of what distinguishes us from most other members of the animal kingdom. We experience joy, sadness, grief, surprise, fear, guilt, anger, awe, shame, hope, and more. Sometimes we experience these in rapid succession, often hitting us with what feels like a tsunami. A wave of sadness or grief hits us, and we feel as though we're going to drown in it. A wave of powerful anger arises, and we want to punch something. A wave of joy emerges, and we try to hold it tightly so it never leaves.

Just as Anil didn't have tools for managing his emotional waves, most of us don't either. Whether we are physicians or not, we don't typically learn how to work with our emotions. We don't see healthy role modeling. We witness parents saying sternly, "We don't do anger in our family. Go to your room and don't come out until you have a smile on your face." Then we are awakened during the night, hearing them in the grips of an angry shouting match. We're left confused and without tools for managing the flow of emotions that are a normal part of daily life.

For physicians, the lack of healthy role modeling continues into our training.[1-2] Without a doubt, our work involves witnessing a great deal of suffering. We tell a 60-year-old about the new mass found on their chest X-ray when they thought they were just coming in to get an antibiotic for their cough. We tell a young couple that their third attempt at pregnancy has resulted in yet another miscarriage. We have to inform a husband that his wife, the mother of their teenage sons, is on a ventilator due to COVID-19. Although we may receive tips on how to break bad news and help patients accept a new diagnosis, we learn little about how to process the array of emotions that arise within us.[3-4]

For Anil, and for all of us physicians, this leaves us stuck, out of balance, and trapped in patterns of reacting to whatever is going on within and around us. Almost like a ping-pong ball, we are batted about by the events of our days, stuck being reactive and not knowing how to do anything else.

Furthermore, we tend to fight the same emotional battles time and time again.

Whether it's around charting or our interactions with our spouse or feeling disrespected by a healthcare system focused more on profit than compassionate care, we regularly experience the same emotional storm over and over. Mindfulness provides the tools to recognize the storm—helping us decide to either go inside knowing a downpour is coming or pop open an umbrella to protect ourselves from getting drenched.

Take a moment now to consider what emotional storms you tend to experience over and over.

Furthermore, when Anil shared that he "zoned out," I knew that he had been triggered into psychological shutdown. Far from willful procrastination, this reaction was caused by his nervous system activating into that painful freeze state of fight/flight/freeze limbic activation. Instead of being triggered by the survival threat of a woolly mammoth or saber-toothed tiger, he had been triggered by the psychological threat of being told he was not doing a good enough job.

This is a common trigger for physicians. A close second is the sense that we're being treated unfairly. A third is that our work and our very selves are not being respected. Given how many physicians identify with being special, this last one can be particularly pervasive, leaving us taking the dysfunctions in healthcare personally when they actually have little to do with us. The things that trigger us may in fact be inherent aspects of this system and not truly indicators of our worth or how others feel about us.

It was a combination of all three that triggered Anil into his pattern of procrastination and inefficiency.

The Life of Our Emotions

Coupled with awareness that all our thoughts are simply transient mental blips, mindfulness helps us realize that our emotions are transient too. Emotions such as sadness, anger, fear, or shame arise, seeming momentous when they occur and often disrupting our next hour, afternoon, or evening. In reality, however, they all dissipate and are no more. Multiple studies confirm this fact.[5-6] Despite this, our emotions determine much of what we humans experience and provide critically important information. They help us communicate with others, act quickly in important situations, empathize with those around us, and make crucial decisions.

But they are still all transient blips. Reading this, you may be thinking: *Now wait a minute. My emotions are more than blips. They are real and powerful—and completely warranted!*

Our emotions can definitely feel like more than blips. And our emotional responses are often seemingly rational responses to what we experience.

However, while they *feel* this way, they actually all pass through. In fact, the neurochemicals that generate our experience of emotions flush through the body in less than 90 seconds. Their half-life is surprisingly short. What keeps the emotion *lasting longer* are the thought loops our minds get caught in—in other words, the very thoughts and stories our minds are so busy producing. And while at times the initial emotional response is warranted, the subsequent ruminations rarely are.

For Anil, anger, frustration, and fear around charting led to worry. Worry led to thoughts. Thoughts led to more fear and worry. Around and around it went, keeping him trapped in a cycle of inefficiency and distress.

Nonetheless, when we can see our emotions for what they are, we can watch the chemical storm generate and pass through without being as caught in it. We can notice that the emotional storms of today are often the same ones as yesterday, and gradually we can detach and view them as outdated patterns of the mind and not reflections of **us**. In observing our emotions and letting them pass through, they lessen, and we can break the cycle of storms we've been caught in for years.

Sadly, Anil's training had not taught him this important skill.

You're likely wondering, *So how do I develop this powerful ability?*

There are three key mindfulness strategies that provide a path to reduced reactivity: Purposeful pauses, becoming the observer, and meditation. All three help create distance between us and our emotional responses. The first two help us when we're in the midst of the storm. The latter is the strategizing and readying we do while the sun is still shining.

Let's take a closer look at each of these now.

The Purposeful Pause

There is so much going on in the physician's day that it can seem as if there is not a moment to stop. There are medication and test prior authorizations, labs to review, patient callbacks, letters, and other inbox responsibilities galore. There are advanced practice nurses to supervise, charts to be done, procedures to be performed, emails to answer, and visits to try to stay on time for. There are urgencies and emergencies, all of which need to be added to an already packed schedule.

All this keeps us in a state of almost constant motion, often with a sense of urgency that makes it difficult to recognize the need to stop and reflect. Combine this with the array of emotions we experience, and it can seem like there is no space to bring calm into the storm.

Constantly moving in this way comes at quite a cost to us and affects our ability to manage our emotions. When we're too busy to pay attention to them, we tend to push them away, and then they spring out and derail us when we least expect them, impacting how we communicate with patients, team members, and others. And, like Anil, we are so caught up in the emotion and attendant thought loops that we don't always appreciate just how much they are impacting us.

Stopping and pausing can powerfully shift this imbalance, enabling us to regulate and pace ourselves much more effectively.

A simple pause, even for the time it takes for three deep breaths, helps us reset. These pauses are so effective that I deem them one of the greatest mindfulness hacks that anyone can incorporate.

With a pause, we're creating that all-important gap between ourselves and our thoughts and emotions. A purposeful pause provides space for the neurochemical cascade to subside so we can then act with greater poise and professionalism.

Pausing helps cool down our limbic state so we can respond and not react.

The practice of taking pauses is now considered so important to successful leadership that it is taught in business school courses. Research by the Institute for Mindful Leadership indicates that when busy corporate leaders incorporate purposeful pauses into their days, they experience not only greater calm but also increased innovation, clarity, and productivity. We are all susceptible to making decisions from a place of emotional reactivity—simply taking a few seconds to reorient helps us acknowledge whatever emotion is at play and move forward from a more rational place.[7]

When I suggested purposeful pauses to Anil, he initially scoffed at the idea. Taking a pause can sound overly simplistic and unscientific to the busy physician. But Anil was feeling so overwhelmed by charting that he was willing to try anything. I instructed him to take a pause after any patient visits he found stressful. "Well, that won't be hard," he told me. "I have a lot of worried well patients in my practice who demand tests for every little headache or stomachache that arises. I'll have plenty of opportunities!"

Purposeful pauses helped Anil slow down and pace himself. They also helped him become the observer of his emotional state, as opposed to being the one caught in it.

Becoming the Observer

When we take purposeful pauses, we make space to become the observer of our inner state. After all, we physicians are trained to be keen observers. The dermatologist notices slight variations in skin thickness, subtle areas of pitting, and nuances of coloration. The rheumatologist observes how the patient moves their left arm as opposed to their right, whether there is subtle wincing with movement, or even a hint of swelling in the joint. The psychiatrist takes in the patient's affect and whether they appear disheveled or well groomed.

Medical training helps us develop this observer lens. In spite of this, though, you have seen that it doesn't train us to apply these same powers of observation to our thoughts, stories, and emotional patterns. Problematically, this can leave us vulnerable to something known as inattentional blindness, with a number of studies confirming this phenomenon.

In one of the most compelling of these, nine radiologists from a prestigious Boston hospital and 15 expert examiners from the American Board of Radiology were asked to perform a familiar task: Identify lung nodules on the CT scans of healthy adults. An image of a gorilla, 48 times larger than the average nodule, was inserted in one of these. While eye tracking revealed that the majority of those who missed the gorilla looked directly at its location, 83 percent of radiologists did not see the gorilla. The conclusion: Even experts, operating in their domain of expertise, are vulnerable to inattentional blindness.[8]

Far from an indictment of expert radiologists, this helps us understand that even the most highly trained minds experience blind spots. In fact, blind spots are part of the human experience for us all.

If you take a moment to test yours by watching this amusing 1-minute video* of two basketball teams passing the ball, you may notice a similar phenomenon.

Watching this video likely verified that we often miss what is in plain sight. It turns out that whether someone in a gorilla suit walks across an engrossing basketball game, or you're driving, on a call, and miss the red light you've just gone through, unless we pay close attention, we can miss even the most conspicuous details. And we're not typically aware that we're not aware of them.

One way we build this awareness is with an exercise often done in introductory mindfulness courses. It involves a seemingly mundane experience: Eating a raisin. Although it may seem like mindful eating has nothing to do with emotional awareness, in fact there is much we can garner from this simple activity.

If you have raisins in your cupboard, you can do this exercise right now. We're going to take 5 minutes just to eat this raisin.

First, we inspect the raisin visually, noticing the contours and areas that are shiny or dull. Next, we involve our sense of smell and bring the raisin to one nostril and then

* - https://www.youtube.com/watch?v=Ahg6qcgoay4

the other. Using our sense of touch, we notice whether the raisin is soft or hard, squishy or firm, moist or dry.

Next, we place the raisin on our tongue and notice the taste. All of this is done very slowly, giving this sensory experience our full attention.

Finally, after chewing in slow motion, you may swallow your raisin.

As odd as this exercise may sound, paying full attention to every detail of a tiny little raisin helps us appreciate how much we miss in daily life as well as just how much of our experience is predominated by thoughts and stories about the experience, rather than the experience of the experience itself.

As we saw earlier, the human mind is like an overly talkative roommate, chatting away to us incessantly. We can begin to appreciate how the mind's flow of thoughts and emotions can also be likened to a waterfall.

If you picture a waterfall right now, you'll see the beauty, the sparkling, the joyful dancing of the water as it cascades down from on high. You'll see the magnificence of this force of nature and want to bask in all its majesty.

But if you were to stand right under the waterfall, you would rapidly become drenched and uncomfortable. That's just not the right way to appreciate a waterfall, is it?

Yet, like Anil, we can be so caught up in our emotions that we can't see them for what they are. To gain agency over the storm of his emotions, Anil needed to step out of the waterfall.

Meditation

To help him do so, I encouraged Anil to begin meditating.

While mindfulness is the awareness we develop when we pay attention to what's here in the present moment, meditation is the primary practice by which we become more mindful.

With meditation, we sit quietly and become the observer of our experience. Additionally, we slow things down and notice what's happening in the moments that are here, right now.

The opposite of the multitasking physicians are used to, with meditation, we are mini-tasking. We're stepping out of all the noise and distractions, and into what is truly going on in our experience. We're seeing firsthand the changing, moment-to-moment swirl of experience. We're seeing that *everything* we experience is transient. Instead of blithely trying to convince ourselves that what we experience will pass, we're *directly witnessing* the passing flow of thoughts, stories, and emotions.

One result of this is that we develop more trust in our own experience. We know for ourselves what is going on. We see that we don't need to look outside for validation and acceptance. As the antithesis of identifying as special and of much of what we learned in our training, we develop greater autonomy over the very ways we view ourselves. We realize that we can appreciate our own strengths without comparing ourselves to others.

For Anil, instead of accusing himself of not being as smart or as efficient as other physicians, he could see more clearly that he was not alone in his charting struggle. This clarity helped replace a sense of powerlessness with more of a sense of mastery and autonomy.

Still, many physicians tell me that they have tried meditation but found they weren't good at it. What they're saying is that their mind was full of thoughts, yet they believed that it was supposed to be quiet. The fact is that the human mind is an extraordinarily busy place! The objective is not to eradicate or banish thought. The objective is simply observing what the mind is up to.

When we meditate, we're actually just doing two simple things:

1. We're noticing when a thought, an emotion, or a physical sensation enters our experience. That, in and of itself, is an act of mindfulness, as we're becoming aware of what is occurring in our mind. We can sharpen this awareness by whispering a gentle mental labeling to ourselves: *Thinking, emotion, sadness, anger,* or *discomfort.*

2. We're using our breath to bring ourselves back from thought and emotion to the physical experience of the present moment. We're training the mind to focus where we want it to focus—in this case, on our breath. The act of breathing, there every moment of our lives, helps us move our attention from the mental event of thought to the physical events of our body, always present in the now.

Our breath serves to anchor us to the here and now.

Our thoughts are not an enemy that we have to fight off in a misguided attempt at mental quietude. Instead, we are honing our powers of observation and simply noticing when a thought or an emotion is present. More like a puff of air than a fierce battle, we simply shift our attention away from the cascade of thoughts and emotions, back to the now. We are building our ability to focus our attention, moment by moment, and simply observe what is going on. By observing whatever we experience as it is, we allow the accumulated pressure behind the emotions to release, and the corresponding thoughts begin to lessen as well.

So, how do you meditate? If we aren't warding off thoughts, what are we doing? For a primer on meditation, you can refer back to the open sky meditation on page 82. At the end of this chapter, there is another meditation for you to try, one on building kindness for ourselves and for others. These exercises will help you build a mindful foundation and become more aware and compassionate.

For more ways to integrate the concepts you've learned in this book and to get started with meditation, you can download my free 14-day mini mindfulness course, *The Daily Dose of Calm.**

Meditation in Action

When Anil started meditating, he was struck by all the negative judgments his mind was making—about himself, his emotions, charting, and more. After meditating for a few weeks, he noticed shifts: "I don't exactly know how to put it into words, Gail," he confided, "but now I can much more easily shift out of anger and irritation to productive action. I can see my emotions for what they are, and I have more agility in letting them pass through. I don't get as caught by them and I don't get wound up about charting like I used to. And since I've been meditating on a regular basis," he went on, "I can access this place more readily. I have a greater sense of what calm looks like, so it's easier to find it when needed. If I'm going into overdrive, hepped up about charting

---

* - https://gailgazelle.com/ddoc-sign-up/

or something else, I realize I can do something about it. I can remind myself to take a purposeful pause and bring myself a degree of calm."

As Anil shared this with me, I breathed my own sigh of relief. I knew that mindfulness would help him gain mastery over the onerous task of charting, and it was wonderful witnessing him see this for himself.

In terms of my own journey with mindfulness, I began meditating regularly 10 years ago. I recall how, initially, I would find myself judging myself, sure that there was something wrong with the way I was breathing, sitting, or maybe even with the expression on my face. My physician mind was so conditioned to judgments and problems that it went to town about my imagined inadequacies as a meditator.

After meditating for many years now, though, the self-judgments have decreased, but it's not as if my mind is miraculously quiet. Far from it! The thoughts and emotions continue to arise, but it's considerably quieter than before, and I have learned to simply be the observer, the one noting what my mind is up to.

It can be quite disarming to see this while meditating. Even the most self-aware physician is often shocked by the relentless cascade of activity.

The good news, though, is that once you see the stream of thoughts, stories, and emotions more clearly, you automatically become better able to work with them. After all, you have to diagnose before you can treat.

Burnout and Being Stuck

A fascinating part of physician burnout is that without realizing it we can find ourselves stuck in a Groundhog Day–like pattern. We get caught in habits of thought and emotion that are unseen from our view. We fight the same battles day in, day out, often without awareness that we're even fighting them. We're stuck in patterns of reactivity and don't see the choice points we have.

This was true for Anil, and it was also true for Mitch, an emergency physician in a busy inner-city trauma center. Between the COVID-19 pandemic, an institutional merger, an increase in gang violence, and the nursing shortage, there was a constant backlog, and neither the doctors nor patients were happy about it. It felt unfair to Mitch, and he found himself frustrated and angry about it all. These emotions generated thoughts: *I can't believe they're making us see all these patients. This is completely unfair. I hate my work.* These thoughts led to more emotions: *This is making me feel anxious and stressed. Who wouldn't be? I am so angry all the time; I feel like I'm going to have an MI.*

The emotions fueled more thoughts: *I have to get out of this job, but what can I do? My family is happy here; my kids are in a good school. It's taken three years to get everyone settled, and my wife will be devastated if we have to pick up and move yet again.*

Round and round it went, the exact same Groundhog Day of misery we saw with Anil.

It all left Mitch depleted. It also left him wondering whether he should get out of medicine completely.

The onslaught of thoughts and emotions also meant that the things that were going well—helping a 20-year-old cocaine-addicted gang member get into rehab or teaching a 4th-year resident how to suture a complex laceration—were out of Mitch's field of view, his mind racing in the swirl of painful thoughts and emotions. In addition to fears about his health, the anger, frustration, and worry were causing him sleepless nights, as well as triggering irritability and distraction when he was at home with his family.

When Mitch began taking purposeful pauses, however, he could see that all the difficulties in his emergency department were ones that other emergency physicians were experiencing as well. He could move from a sense that it was just him who was being treated poorly to the larger truth: Overstretched and understaffed urban EDs were becoming the norm. Seeing this bigger picture more clearly, he was able to step out of taking it all as a personal affront. Instead of being triggered by feeling disrespected—something that only fueled more emotion—Mitch moved to agency in how he responded to the challenges.

Mitch wanted to try meditation and asked me if he should start with an hour. Knowing that his life was full with busy shifts and young kids, I shared guidance I once heard from physician mindfulness colleague Ron Epstein in his masterful *Mindful Practice* program. Knowing how physicians naturally respect medical jargon, Ron jokingly suggests that busy physicians begin meditating with a low dose of 2 minutes a day and then titrate up as tolerated.

Like others, Mitch was initially shocked by what he found. But gradually increasing from 2 to 15 minutes daily, he could observe the thoughts and emotions as they arose in his mind. He realized that they all passed, helping him be less gripped by each and every one of them.

Mitch had started the process of moving from servant of his mind to master. He felt relaxed after meditating, and it helped set a better tone for the day. He told me, "I'm so used to going at 110 percent. Now, somehow, I'm going a little bit more slowly. Same overcrowded ER, same mix of difficult patients, same understaffing, but I'm not getting blown off course anywhere near as readily as I did before."

When Anil and Mitch applied their powers of observation, they also learned that they could quiet their minds, steadying themselves despite all that was going on around them.

As you see in these examples, mindful awareness brings our thoughts and feelings out of unconscious and automatic patterning into the light of day, where we can observe them more closely. And just like the unseen gorilla, we often find a multitude of blind spots.

As we sit in meditation and focus our attention on what is going on within us, we also become aware of just how much is going well, no matter what is not. This awareness helps us appreciate the blessings in our lives, and also brings awareness to smaller miracles that we don't typically appreciate. We realize that every time our body exhales, it naturally inhales without any effort on our part, something we rarely stop to appreciate. Similarly, our heart is beating regularly, delivering precious oxygen and other nutrients to all our cells. With an average heart rate of 70 beats per minute, this occurs approximately 100,000 times a day and about 35 million times a year. Even as physicians, we have to admit just how wondrous the workings of our bodies truly are.

When we focus inward, in a sense we are tuning out all the distractions that populate our days—from phones, TV, emails, texts, the internet, and the typical discourse we engage in. Even though we don't always realize how our minds are fielding all these inputs, in truth, the barrage of information creates a state of continuous partial attention. With meditation, we're hitting the pause button on all of that noise, going inward, and embracing what is present in this moment.

We are learning that this moment matters—this one right now.

As Mitch saw all the benefits for himself, he wanted to share them with his staff. Reviewing many studies, he learned about the benefits of meditation. He saw it demonstrated that meditation decreases stress, anxiety, and the chronic inflammation that stress is known to induce.[9-13] He learned how meditation decreases depression and the neurochemical factors that fuel it.[14-15]

He looked at the evidence supporting claims of meditation increasing focus[16] and memory,[17] as well as decreasing rumination.[18-20]

He read studies demonstrating the salutary impact of even brief weeks of meditation on controlling blood pressure,[21-22] decreasing chronic pain,[23-24] and decreasing predisposition to Alzheimer's disease.[25]

Mitch also saw the numerous studies concluding that mindfulness decreases physician burnout.

As a matter of fact, as of the writing of this book, there are over two dozen published studies on mindfulness interventions and physician burnout, spanning a wide variety of specialties from internal medicine to ear, nose, and throat surgery to palliative care to pediatric oncology and ophthalmology.[26-39]

Covering trainees as well as attending physicians, a systematic review looked at 25 studies that included over 900 physician subjects[40] and six randomized controlled trials.[41-46] There were significant reductions in levels of burnout and stress reported.

With all these upsides, Mitch was excited to introduce meditation to the physicians he oversaw.

One of them, Priya, was struggling to keep up with the high patient volumes they were encountering. Like many mid-career emergency physicians, the adrenaline that had fueled her for decades was now running thin. She found herself experiencing the same pre-shift dread as Mitch, and her circadian rhythms had been so disrupted by years of variable day and night adjustments that she suffered from chronic insomnia. Often tossing and turning in bed, she would find herself replaying difficult interactions, worrying that she had missed something, and fretting about patient outcomes. The swell of thoughts and emotions left her irritable and reactive. She knew that if she didn't do something, she was at risk for acting in ways she would later regret.

After meditating for a few weeks, Priya reported to Mitch that things had begun to shift. She was able to quiet her thoughts and emotions. She found that she was sleeping a bit better. She could observe the dread and let that pass through as well. Meditation wasn't a panacea, of course, but it helped her work more effectively with the stresses of her work.

Taking purposeful pauses, becoming the observer, and meditating helped Anil, Mitch, and Priya leave their patterns of inattentional blindness. By stepping out of their inherent biases and assumptions, and becoming aware of their recurring emotional storms and reactions, they each experienced reduced reactivity and moved to a place where the view was refreshingly clear. For it is not until we become curious about these blind spots that we can fully see them for what they are. When we can't see (read: diagnose) our sticking points and their sources, how can we possibly work with them?

MINDFULNESS EXERCISE: TAKING A PURPOSEFUL PAUSE

Your days are busy with a lot coming at you, and you may be used to a lot of multitasking. You may find that your days go by in a blur.

Stopping and taking a purposeful pause can help you reset, regroup, and bring calm to your experience. It can help you step out of the fray and move to the stance of the observer, where you will likely find more clarity regarding the best way to proceed.

Here is a 4-step process for taking a purposeful pause when you notice emotions or stress responses boiling over.

1. Pause.

Stop whatever you are doing, physically and mentally. Turn your attention to what is present right now. Orient yourself to the present moment by noticing the sensation of your feet on the floor and your back against the chair. Take in one thing in your visual field.

2. Breathe.

Take three slow, deep breaths. Allow your breath to anchor you to the present.

3. Listen.

Give your full attention to your inner state, listening deeply to whatever your experience is in this moment.

4. Be kind to yourself.

Place your right hand over the left side of your chest where your heart resides.

Try to step out of any negative judgments toward yourself. Remind yourself of how hard you're working and praise yourself for your efforts.

See if you can take purposeful pauses a few times a day. You will find these bring greater calm to your days—and greater clarity as well.

Q AND A

1. I like the idea of taking purposeful pauses, but my days are so packed with all the patients they keep adding on. How can I possibly fit pauses in?

I'll share a mindfulness adage: If you don't have time to meditate for 5 minutes, then you probably need to meditate for an hour. In short—you feeling like you barely have time to pause is exactly why you need to start pausing!

But your concern is one that many people have, well beyond the medical profession. The demands of modern work can be so numerous that it can feel like there isn't time to do anything but put our nose to the grindstone and get everything done. Unfortunately, this can leave us feeling like a spinning top, in constant mindless motion.

In reality, a purposeful pause only takes less than a minute! While at first glance it seems as if there is no time to add them in, perhaps that is just a story your mind is telling you.

What I recommend is starting with taking two pauses every day. You can even put these on your calendar, inserting them in places where you can anticipate a need for decreasing stress.

As you get comfortable taking pauses, you'll see the tremendous benefit they provide. You can then add from there.

2. You talk about being in the present moment, but what's wrong with revisiting a difficult case or planning my next vacation?

There is nothing wrong with thinking about the past or future. What's problematic is when our mind does so involuntarily. As you start paying attention, you'll notice just how much our minds jump around. We're working on a project, and we find our mind replaying an argument we had with our in-laws or something someone said that we found upsetting. Or we finally are home from a long day at work, sitting at dinner with our family, and our mind gets lost thinking about charts we have to get done (or the bills we have to pay) later that night.

All this mental activity keeps us from being present in the moments of our lives and leaves us scattered, unfocused, and unhappy.

With mindful attention, we gain autonomy over our minds and can redirect ourselves much more readily. We can then be more present with those we interact with, helping them feel more seen and appreciated, something we all deserve to experience.

3. I am like Anil: I can't stand doing my charts. How do I deal with the fact that when I sit down to chart, all I can think about is how unfair it all is?

I can see why you feel this way, and I'm not going to argue about the question of fairness. There is much in our jobs that could be considered unfair, whether we are physicians or in most any other line of work. At the same time, I suspect you'll agree that the task of charting is here to stay. No amount of disliking charting is going to make it go away.

Recall, moreover, what Carl Jung had to say: What we resist persists. The more we resist a task, the more emotional dissonance we develop, and then the harder it is to get the darn task done!

In our fifth way, we'll be looking at working with what is—not what we wish was different, but the reality of what is. In the meantime, continue to the next chapter and you'll gain greater insights and skills that will help you with charting—and more.

4. LEAN INTO COMPASSION, CONNECTION, AND PURPOSE

"If you want others to be happy, practice compassion.
If you want to be happy, practice compassion."
—Dalai Lama

When he walked into the patient's room, Raoul wasn't sure he could muster up the energy to have the conversation. It was late June, and, coming to the end of the second year of his neurology residency, he felt like he was burnt to a crisp.

Raoul had spent his teen years watching his mother suffer the ravages of multiple sclerosis. She had gone from active and healthy to having difficulty walking to requiring care just to get dressed and fed. A devoted son, he had accompanied her on medical visits and seen how much the attentiveness and compassion of her physicians had helped her, even when there were no medications that could. It was this that drew him first to medical school and then to his choice of neurology as a specialty.

But thus far in his residency, he had learned the hard way that he always needed to have the right answer and that he could be thrown under the bus if he didn't. The long hours, combined with having to hide emotion or weakness, were wearing him down. He'd stopped exercising, his nails were bitten to the quick, and his girlfriend had told him that she was fed up with hearing all his complaints.

Raoul was so burned out that he wasn't sure he could stay in medicine. Despite having $300,000 in student loans, he had dreams of leaving medicine and becoming a librarian in a small town, where he could get away from all this stress.

His patient was an elderly woman hospitalized after a massive stroke. The matriarch of a large Colombian family, she now lay paralyzed on the right side and unresponsive, reduced to complete dependence on others for all bodily needs. It was apparent to the team that her chances of surviving were slim.

Raoul's team had an unusually high census of patients to care for, but Raoul had seen how distressed the patient's family was and made sure to meet with them after rounds. Sitting with the daughter, three sons, and son-in-law for an hour, he translated medical jargon, provided information about her prognosis, and listened intently to their hopes and fears.

As painful as it was for them to face, the family was able to see that their mother would not want to be kept alive in this state. It was an intense meeting, but Raoul was able to help them move from despair to a sense of peace that her time had come.

Tired as he was, Raoul left the hospital with a feeling of pride. Instead of his typical gripes, he told his girlfriend how good it felt to be there for this family.

"This is why I went into medicine in the first place," he said. *Maybe I did make the right choice*, he thought.

Compassion in Healthcare

It was compassion that helped Raoul find a way forward, and it is compassion that binds the interwoven fabric of healthcare. After all, healthcare is the profoundly human endeavor of caring for others when they are facing something gone awry with their health. Seeing and attending to the suffering of others is what healthcare is all about.

This takes us to the fourth way mindfulness restores your autonomy and cures healthcare burnout: Rekindling and leaning into compassion, connection, and sense of purpose.

It is likely compassion and connection that drew you to the profession of medicine in the first place.

However, as we continue in our careers, through the multitude of challenges of modern practice, compassion can fall by the wayside. The fabric that holds healthcare together can become loose and frayed.

Indeed, all the demands and pressures clinicians experience can shift our focus away from the difficulties our patients are experiencing. This includes all the administrative demands, the long hours at the job, and the inherent uncertainty and unpredictability of outcomes. Like a frog in a pot of boiling water, as all the changes in healthcare whittle away at us, we can wake up one day having lost the purpose, compassion, and resolve that we had when we first donned our white coat (or hopped into the pot).

Being a physician is taxing. In addition to all the shifts corporatization has brought, it includes an almost constant exposure to illness and trauma, the burden of delivering bad news, and the moral distress when we know what is right to do but are so over-taxed that it's hard to do it. Or when we are directly incentivized to do the opposite.

Not surprisingly, all of these can interfere with our ability to be present, caring, and compassionate to those in need. They can deplete our compassion reserves and wear down even the most caring among us.

This wearing thin of compassion is detrimental to our patients—perhaps obviously so. Moments of connection and compassion like Raoul's are crucial for the patients and families we take care of. What may be less obvious is just how detrimental the loss of compassion is for us as well.

Losing compassion and purpose puts us on a fast track toward burnout.[1-2] Raoul's connection with this family provided a powerful salve for his dissatisfaction and loss of purpose. Just this one caring encounter with a family facing the tragic loss of their beloved mother helped restore his sense of purpose and satisfaction. Without these restorative moments, our work becomes flat, uninspiring, and devoid of humanity. It becomes disconnected from true meaning and purpose. Recall that we saw this earlier with Dianna, the endocrinologist who was stuck in a story that her practice was boring, tedious, and miserable.

Conversely, when we deeply tap into the purpose and compassion of serving others, we heal our own burnout and reinvigorate ourselves as healers. Importantly, this requires focusing on the parts that we can control—ourselves and our interactions. It requires being sure to take in the good we are doing and shifting focus away from all that is not going well. It involves stepping out of the ever-present waterfall of thoughts, stories, and emotions we tend to get caught in. It involves mastering our patterns of reactivity.

These mindfulness measures facilitate our being fully present and compassionate with the vulnerable patients in front of us.

At the same time, why is it that in our training, and in the overall healthcare system, compassion falls by the wayside?

Most notably, healthcare operates in a society that tends to undervalue compassion, where the focus is more on competition, profit, and productivity. In the Western world, we typically value money more than time, personal advancement more than societal improvement, and individual material gain more than that of our communities.

These societal forces do not spare healthcare. In many ways healthcare simply provides a mirror reflecting back the challenges apparent in so many areas of culture and society. (Methinks that's a good topic for another book 😄).

Ubiquitous to all modern and historic religions, however, compassion is a core tenet of humanity. Research also reveals that compassion is something that is innate to human beings; it's something we are born with. It's a feeling we have when we encounter the pain and suffering of others; for most of us, we find ourselves moved to do something to alleviate their distress, if we have the capability to do so.

It's a motivation that even the tiniest child has toward others. Studies have shown that infants as young as 2 years old are socially interested in and attentive to other infants who are crying. Well before we are old enough to take care of ourselves, we are moved to take care of others.[3-6]

After all, we are a social species, and pro-social motivation is vital for our survival. If we hadn't banded together in prehistoric times to protect ourselves and tribemates, gather food, and fight attackers, we would not have prevailed as a species.

Not only is compassion vital for our survival, but it is also positively correlated with better health, well-being, and happiness within ourselves and in our relationships. In fact, compassion has been positively associated with a stabilized heart rate, increased oxytocin release, and improved immune function.[7-8] It is the dearth of these positive biologic responses that is avid fuel for burnout.

Compassion: Here and Gone

As we have seen, many of the difficulties in the modern healthcare environment contribute to a physician's loss of purpose and compassion, as there is no question that physicians start off as some of the most compassionate beings on the planet. We enter medical training full of a desire to alleviate illness and suffering, and we begin with a great deal of compassion toward our patients. Our very calling is to help others in their time of vulnerability and need.

But after entering the profession and seeing mental, physical, and emotional suffering of every possible kind and working long hours with little rest, many find their compassion buried under overwhelm and burnout. Even before assuming the responsibility of being a full-fledged physician, the compassion of medical students is all too often chipped away.[9-12]

Why is this the case?

In addition to the long hours, physical exhaustion, and vicarious traumatization of medical student life, there are four key reasons.

1. Compassion is **undervalued** in medical training. The emphasis is on knowledge, facts, and certainty (even when uncertainty prevails). The scientific takes precedence over the human, keeping medical trainees focused more on matters of the mind than those of the heart.[13-15] Since compassion is considered "soft," it can mistakenly be categorized as ancillary to the mission of science and cure.

2. The hidden curriculum includes a belief that **detachment** is necessary to endure the hardships one witnesses, often day in, day out.[16-18] In other words, physicians are implicitly taught to keep a firm barrier between themselves and their patients' suffering. While it is important not to shoulder the emotional burden of our patients, as healers we need to at least affirm and support our patients through it. A mindless detachment from the suffering in front of us positions our patients as case studies and exam questions instead of as human beings we care for.

When we detach from the suffering of others, we can also detach from the sense of meaning and purpose that led us to want to alleviate suffering in the first place.[19] For Raoul, going out of his way to be there for a family in need reconnected him with his purpose, the all-important "why" of his work.

3. The **problem-focused lens** takes us away from positivity and compassion. Although this diagnostic lens helps us spot and target illnesses and the pathologic processes that cause them, when over-applied, it leads us to miss all that is going well in the human body and mind. This negative focus erodes the compassion that took us into our careers.

4. Most importantly, as we've seen, many aspects of training instill a **sense of fear**. Fear that our imperfections will be seen by others. Fear that we will be shamed for making a mistake. Fear that we will be judged harshly, compared with our peers, and found wanting.[20-22] When we are mired in fear and scarcity, the last thing we feel compelled to do is extend compassion to others. Our cup feels empty so we are reluctant to pour into anyone else's. Ironically, these moments of compassion and focus on others, like the one Raoul experienced, sustain us and help us refill our own energy stores.

Agnes, a 4th-year med student, put it this way: "I only have so much energy and I feel so downtrodden by the constant fear of not measuring up. I notice that I'm thinking about myself the whole day. I barely have the energy to take care of me, let alone all of my patients."

This final factor, fear, holds our natural compassion hostage. Brought forth by a training focused more on comparisons and criticism than on strengths and accomplishments, fear is the antithesis of compassion and connection. When we're in fear, our survival brain is activated. Instead of reaching out to others, we hunker down. Fear takes us to our small selves, to a place of scarcity, to a place where we have to defend ourselves and our turf.

Unfortunately, inhabiting this place of fear and survival only depletes us further.

But when we move from fear to compassion, we thrive mentally and physically. Modern advances in neuroscience help us understand why it feels good to be compassionate. When fMRI scans were taken of experienced meditators as they generated strong feelings of compassion, there was an increase in activity in the left side of the prefrontal cortex where positive emotions—happiness, confidence, and hopefulness—arise, and a decrease in activity on the right side where negative states—anxiety and depression—are registered.[23-24] Similarly, when we help a neighbor, a stranger, or someone who is homeless, we experience a rush of dopamine and serotonin, the neurotransmitters tied to reward and pleasure.[25-27]

Furthermore, when we help others, we shift our focus from our own suffering and difficulties to those of the person in need. We shift from an overly self-focused sphere, one where we are preoccupied with our own challenges, to something more broad. We move from the small self to a larger, more expansive one. Shifting from an overly self-focused sense to a broader sense of shared humanity, we shrink our own challenges. By not making our problems the center of our reality, we can find that they often fade away.

These positive effects are no less present for physicians, and, not surprisingly, numerous studies confirm that a compassionate approach to patients results in positive outcomes. Not just for patients, but for clinicians as well, correlating with increased job satisfaction, more engagement, and lower rates of burnout in physicians and nurses alike.[28-31] When physicians move from isolation in the small self to compassion for others, they experience increased connection and fulfillment.

More Alike Than Different

This connection and fulfillment hinges upon realizing that the people around us are more similar to us than we typically realize. When we step out of thoughts, stories, patterns of reactivity, and fear-based thinking and step into compassion, purpose, and our true calling as healers, we begin to see the truth: We are all much more alike than different.

Stepping out of our thoughts, stories, patterns of reactivity, and the fear-based thinking instilled in our training, we see this more clearly.

Sadly, the natural outcome of our sense of being special combined with many of the flaws of our training (namely competition, comparisons, perfectionism, and never showing weakness) is separation between us and those around us. While our expertise is not to be discarded, in many ways, this separation leaves us on a psychological team of one, isolated and detached from those around us. Add in a broken healthcare system with misaligned incentives, and this solitary state rolls out the red carpet for burnout.

So how do we foster greater connection in our work and move past these feelings of separateness? We start by leaning into our shared humanity.

After all, we all experience change and uncertainty in our lives. We all experience suffering, in one form or another. We all experience the vulnerability of our human bodies—illness, accidents, and the loss of those we hold dear. We all experience joy, sorrow, and grief.

We all want to be happy and satisfied in our lives. We all want to provide for our loved ones so they have what they need to thrive in their lives. We all want our children to be safe and protected, and to grow into their full potential. We all have goals and aspirations.

Additionally, we all want to be seen for the special and worthy person we are, and for all the good we bring to those around us. We all want to have autonomy over ourselves.

These similarities are the truth of the human condition. With mindfulness, we see this more clearly.

When we can begin to view those around us as partners on this journey called life and recognize that they are just like us, we can move past a scarcity mentality and zero-sum games. We can unlock a deep inner compassion that moves us toward deeper connection and powers us past burnout.

Of course, reaching this level of connection means we need to learn to extend the same compassion we give to those around us, to ourselves. This means learning to quiet our inner critic.

The Inner Critic

The inner critic is exactly what it sounds like.

It's the voice that tells us that we're not smart enough, attractive enough, articulate enough, and a host of other messages of inadequacy and blame. This voice is like an inner bully, ready to pick on us many times a day. For many, it is our backdrop—a tune playing in the background throughout the day. Without tactics to quiet the inner critic, we are left at the mercy of this shrill, mean, and punitive inner judge.

While nearly everyone deals with an inner critic to some degree, because of the fixed medical mindset and the pitfalls of training we have examined, the physician's inner critic can be especially loud and savage in its messaging.

Take Ayesha, a 42-year-old family physician who often ran behind in clinic. She loved taking care of patients, but getting the charts done, as for Anil and many others, was something she hated doing. Moreover, no sooner did she log on to the electronic health record than she found herself besieged by chastising voices: *What's wrong with you, anyway? You're so lazy. Everyone else is so much better at this than you are. You've always been slower than others. I don't even know why you bother trying.*

These voices cut through Ayesha, causing her mood to rapidly plummet and leaving her feeling heavy and defeated. Whatever motivation she might have had to get her charts done rapidly disappeared, and the next thing she knew, she was checking Facebook, stopping to file her nails, and going over the family shopping list—anything but facing this mean, bullying voice that stood between her and getting her charts done.

You may be able to relate to Ayesha's experience. Many physicians experience a similarly harsh inner critic:

- Joon, an anesthesiologist and pain physician of 30 years, was invited to take on the leadership of the palliative care consultation service at his hospital. As a seasoned, white-haired clinician, he was worried because the trainees and most of the attending physicians were young and, as he put it, "closer to training and clearly smarter than me." His inner critic went to town with this, barraging him with nasty jabs: *They're so much smarter than you. What are you even doing in this job? With kids this smart, how could you possibly be their leader? It's time to hang it up.*

- As for Candace, a gynecology researcher at a prestigious southern academic institution and first author on numerous papers, her inner critic told her that her ideas were unoriginal, that other people were better researchers than she was, and, in fact, that she had some sort of fundamental flaw that would keep her from ever being successful. When writing grant proposals, that mean inner voice repetitively went after her: *Who do you think you are, anyway? You've never been as good as others. You'll never make it to the top.*

As with Ayesha, these messages fueled procrastination. Instead of working on her proposals, she'd find herself going on Twitter, where her focus almost invariably took her to tweets others had posted about their successful grants and publications. Social media served to cement her inner critic's view that others' work was successful, and hers was not.

- Jacob's inner critic had a feeding frenzy when he received a diagnosis of celiac disease. Along with fear regarding what might happen with his health, this 46-year-old orthopedist was catapulted into a harsh inner dialogue about the difficulty he was having coping with this new diagnosis. *Why are you reacting this way?* his inner critic demanded. *You're a physician, dammit! You, of all people, should understand that it's simply an illness and that even physicians get illnesses.*

Quieting the Inner Critic, Building Self-Compassion

Like hypertension—often referred to as a silent killer—these harsh inner voices are lethal to our well-being. The critic operates in the background, barely noticed, yet constantly eroding our confidence and efficacy. Forever focused on flaws and other perceived inadequacies, the critic's messages eat at our sense of meaning and purpose. They fuel a downward spiral of self-doubt, self-criticism, and questioning of one's self-worth. Instead of focusing on all the good they are doing, these critical inner voices maintain the physician's focus on just the opposite.

Like the euphemistic death by a thousand cuts, the inner critic slowly whittles away our compassion for others and ourselves. While it may sound obvious, it's hard to maintain a sense of purpose when your mind is busy beating you up.

Further, the worst part of this is that we were never provided the tools we need to defend ourselves. Medical training doesn't teach us how to work with these bullying inner voices, or even to recognize that they aren't us. Instead, as we've seen, it instills a problem-focused pattern of self-criticism and comparison that leaves us discouraged and depleted.

The good news here is that we can learn to quiet the inner critic. The 6 ways you are learning are how the mind training of mindfulness plays a pivotal role in helping us do so.

The first step in this process is moving these voices from the background, where they are typically operating unseen, into the foreground of awareness. In becoming the observer of our minds, we can move these voices from the closed internal chamber of the mind into the light of day. It's that same diagnostic function mentioned earlier. Simply being aware of our patterns is a powerful step in shifting them.

In this first step, I encouraged Ayesha to keep a running list of her inner critic's proclamations. She told me how painful it was to look directly at these nasty voices. Reluctantly, however, she agreed.

She returned for her next coaching session with quite a long list:

- *You've never had what it takes to be a doctor.*
- *You've always been at the bottom of the pack.*
- *Everyone else in your department is smarter than you.*
- *Just face it: You're a bad doctor, a bad parent, and a failure.*
- *You've never been good enough.*

She looked down as she read her list out loud, enshrouded in shame. She had never shared these thoughts with anyone, let alone with another physician. I made sure to tell her just how much courage she was exhibiting, reinforcing that instead of this being something shameful or weak, sharing these was actually evidence of her strength. Clearing out the shame associated with these emotions is necessary to move past them—for Ayesha, this meant sharing them with me and bringing them out of the darkness within.

The second step is seeing the voices for what they are: The misguided proclamations of our judging mind, randomly generated blips from a part of our brain created long ago to keep us alive. Nothing more. Instead of believing these are part of us, we need to create distance between ourselves and the critic. The amygdala is designed to perceive threats, and the inner critic is merely a malfunction of this important survival mechanism. By recognizing these harsh inner thoughts as such, we're creating the all-important mindful gap that helped Anil rightsize his thoughts and emotions.

We're learning to separate the thought from the thinker.

These voices are often the internalization of criticism we have received in the past. They may stem from the words of a parent, a harsh teacher, or a bully from as far back as grade school. Or the sneering voice of a piano teacher or coach, comparing us to another student and finding us wanting. For many, the source of these critical messages is internalized societal scripts around race, gender, sexual orientation, and more.

In fact, these inner critical voices are often a cluster of messages we've heard or told ourselves over the years, internalized and knit together into a painful chorus of personal inadequacy. Occurring repetitively and unchallenged over many days, weeks, months, and years, they become so familiar and ingrained that we begin to believe them to be the one and only truth. Sadly, the constant flow of these thoughts over time crafts a wide and deep crevice in the fabric of our being.

I've noticed that for physicians, the initial drip in this faucet is often the voice of someone senior to us who criticized us for something we didn't know. The deficit and perfection focus of medical training is costly—not only does it make it almost impossible for physicians to focus on our strengths, but it also fuels this pattern of negative self-judgment. The culture of ratings, comparisons, and rankings leaves the physician vulnerable, and deep-seated inner criticism is one very natural sequela. We internalize the comparisons and rankings, taking on the mantle of judgment and criticism. We are good learners, and we believe what our superiors say.

In Ayesha's case, the voice was her chief resident from her internship year, who was convinced that her skills were lacking and regularly pushed her beyond her limits until one day she broke down and began to cry. The chief resident's microaggressions left her so embarrassed that she left rounds and had a hard time returning.

The impact of all the inner and outer put-downs was that when Ayesha sat down to chart, her mind did not go to the elderly patient and her family, who she had helped to understand how to manage the patient's cognitive decline. Her mind did not go to a patient of six years she had supported in coming off chronic opioid use, getting clean and sober for the first time in his adult life. Nor did it go to the countless members of her community she had given medical advice to when meeting them at church or the grocery store. Instead, it went to just about everything she had ever done wrong.

This pattern of focusing on the messages of her inner critic made it almost impossible for Ayesha to be compassionate toward herself.

It was a pattern we needed to shift.

After making the running list and seeing the voices for what they are, in **the third step**, we need to examine and question these thoughts. When these self-critical statements arise, pose three questions to yourself (similar to the questions we ask about the stories our minds tell):

- Is the message objectively true?
- Is it true 100 percent of the time?
- What is one counterexample?

The fourth and final step involves a mantra I've developed that helps solidify kindness to ourselves. The physicians I work with have found this immensely helpful in quieting their inner critics and accepting their foibles and imperfections.

I am good
I do my best
I cannot control
All the rest

Neuroplasticity

Moving away from harsh patterns of self-judgement means rewiring our brain's circuitry, which takes work and repetition. That is all the inner critic is: Neuronal wiring that is locked in a negative, critical inner pattern.[32-33] In replacing these messages with ones that are more accurate, we are rerouting the crevices of synaptic patterns that have been carved into the brain's circuitry—a product of the repetitive thought patterning we've experienced over days, weeks, and even decades.

Harsh self-judgment activates the brain's threat defense system—the same fight/flight/freeze limbic mechanism now so attuned to psychological assault.[34–35] We can juxtapose our self-critical thoughts with a very different system: The mammalian caregiving system. Sometimes called the tend-and-befriend system, this is another key system that evolved to keep us safe from danger. After all, mammals are born unable to care for themselves. They require care and nurturance that typically comes from the mother. Mothers instinctually care for their young, feeding them, keeping them warm, soothing them, comforting them, and protecting them from predators.

When we move from inner criticism to the same caring and compassion we bring to others, we're moving from threat defense to care, leading to a sense of safety, acceptance, and comfort.[36] Extending that care to ourselves is the fastest way to return to a place where we can fully do the same for our patients.

While it took practice, Ayesha began to see that most of these inner messages were not true. It was much harder for her, however, to counter them with something more realistic and affirming.

I could see that we needed to build her muscle of self-compassion.

Our Most Important Patient: Ourselves

With self-compassion, we're shifting the lens from outward to inward caring. We are including ourselves in the group of people who receive care, love, forgiveness, and attention. This is not what most of us in medicine learn. We learn, instead, to put others first, to always be there for our patients—no matter the time of day, and no matter how fatigued and drained we might be. In learning to be experts in the care of others, we don't learn how to apply that same nurturance to ourselves.

Unfortunately, this, like our identity as special, leaves us looking to others to validate and affirm our worth. In the words of mindfulness educator Sharon Salzberg, "When we experience inner impoverishment, love for another too easily becomes hunger: for reassurance, for acclaim, for affirmation of worth."[37]

When Ayesha first started utilizing self-compassion, she said that it felt artificial.

"I didn't believe any of it. In fact, it seemed like a complete farce. But I kept at it. And now, I certainly don't fully believe it 100 percent, but I am starting to believe it a little bit. Maybe that will continue to grow."

We may also think self-compassion is the same as self-pity, that it is self-centered and will encourage us to wallow in ourselves—basically sitting around all day complaining and eating bonbons. But when you stop and think about it, isn't it self-centered to be focused on ourselves and all our perceived faults?

Interestingly, when we are kinder to ourselves, there's often a sense of expansiveness. We are actually less stingy in the compassion we offer to others. Even the scarcity that comes from identifying as special lessens, replaced by an abundance mindset that allows greater compassion for others.

As Ayesha began to build her muscle of self-compassion, she also noticed something shifting in her level of motivation. Instead of sitting at her computer procrastinating, typing a few words and then checking social media, she now found herself better able to get the charts done.

In being kinder to herself, she moved into a greater level of efficacy and efficiency. No longer under the thumb of the inner critic, her fear of inner censure abated and she was more able to get her work done. Slowly, slowly, slowly, and then all at once (how mindfulness progress often works), Ayesha had cast her inner critic aside.

In her next coaching session, Ayesha reported, "In some ways it's subtle, but I notice that I'm much more content at the end of each day. I have more emotional energy to get the work done. I am also noticing that I've been much more patient with my 16-year-old son, and I'm less reactive with him. As I develop more compassion for myself, I seem to have more for others as well."

Mindfully Cultivating Compassion

I am often asked how mindfulness supports compassion. Let me share an anecdote from my own practice that begins with trepidation around attending my first weeklong silent meditation retreat.

Alone with my thoughts for seven whole days, I'll die from boredom, my mind rebelled. *I'll go stir-crazy just sitting in silence for seven whole days. How will I manage?*

But (and this mindfulness expert shouldn't be surprised) it turned out that the experience was completely different from the story my mind had created about it.

As I sat in silence, I noticed not only just how busy my mind was but also all the judgments my mind was spewing out right, left, and center: Judgments about myself, about how I was doing in my meditation, and even judgments comparing my attire to what the other meditators were wearing! I noticed the stories my mind was busy producing about past interactions, future plans, imagined future catastrophes, and everything in between. Instead of being completely bored, I found observing the shenanigans my mind was up to quite humorous and engaging. I also found that by deepening my awareness, it became easier to let the judgments and stories pass through my mind without attaching to them in the way I typically did.

When I returned home, another thing that struck me was how much kinder, more open, more present, and more compassionate I felt. When on my morning dog walk, for example, instead of my usual preoccupation with my thoughts, I was now taking in the colors of the leaves and sky. When I passed others on the street, I smiled at them instead of scowling or not making any sign of recognizing their presence. In response, they often smiled back, uplifting both them and me in the process.

Further, I hadn't realized just how caught my mind had been in a series of negative, repetitive thoughts. In fact, on many prior dog walks, I'd had an argument playing in my head with a friend I tended to label as lazy—sometimes even having mental arguments with her while I could have been relaxing and enjoying the fresh spring air. Quite honestly, it was only after sitting quietly and meditating at length that this repetitive thought pattern became apparent to me.

After a week of sitting silently, my mind was nowhere near as caught by all its former negativity and judgments. With that clarity (read: diagnosis), I could also see just how much misery my own mind was causing me. After all, these mental judgments and arguments were doing nothing to change my friend's behavior—and they certainly were not making me a better friend. Or any happier, for that matter.

Expanding on our definition of mindfulness, we can add that it is the awareness that emerges from paying attention to what's going on in the present moment *in a nonjudgmental fashion*. In other words, mindfulness involves putting aside all the judgments the human mind is so good at producing, about oneself and about others. As we have seen, when we stop and pay attention, our minds are busy producing judgments about just about everything we encounter.

When we employ mindful awareness to work with that almost continuous flow of judgment, we very naturally make room for greater kindness and compassion. The loving kindness meditation outlined at the end of this chapter helps orient us in the right direction, but you may also begin to see that kindness and compassion are our natural state when we clear away judgment and criticism.

In addition to paying attention, this definition of mindfulness points to the importance of *how* we pay attention. We can do so in a critical and narrow way, or we can do so with an open and gentle quality of expansiveness, curiosity, and compassion. When we are mindful, we bring a quality of interest to our experience. We can bring this same quality not just to what's around us, but to others and to ourselves as well.

Imagine, for a moment, a child looking at insects in a field of flowers. The child is fully engaged, open, receptive, curious, and excited by this act of exploration and learning. If we, the adult, walked through that very same field, we'd likely be preoccupied, impatient, rushing to get somewhere else, and full of judgments about how tall the grass was or that the flowers were past their bloom. Perhaps we'd be on our phone, distracted and eager to get to to a moment our mind tells us is going to be a better one.

Yet, it is the child who is more mindful than the impatient adult. Through this quality of newness and receptivity (often referred to as beginner's mind)—of seeing each experience through the lens of a learner—mindful awareness can help us restore that sense of openness, curiosity, and interest many of us shed long ago.

At the same time, with mindful awareness we build our ability to step out of the thoughts and stories we are all too often entrapped by, and we can be more present with exactly what is happening right in front of us. No matter how busy our days, we can step out of the place of negativity that these mental stories typically take us to. As we step out of judgment, we have more capacity to actually be present with those we interact with and to move toward alleviating their duress.

This is true for what we bring to our patients, and it is true well beyond how we relate in the workplace. The physicians I coach who put concerted effort into building this muscle report better friendships, marriages, and relationships with their children. In many cases, this is because they have quieted their inner critic and now experience less negative judgment toward themselves. The science is clear: Less negative judgment toward ourselves leads to less judgment toward others.[38-40]

It's interesting and somewhat paradoxical that being good to yourself actually helps you be more engaged and less exhausted with your work, whereas the converse only gets in the way. In fact, while research on self-compassion in physicians is still a new area of exploration, a 2019 study found that self-compassionate physicians experienced more positive work engagement, felt less emotionally, physically, and cognitively exhausted due to work demands, and were more satisfied with their professional life than physicians who exhibited less compassion toward themselves in uncertain and challenging times.[41]

But self-compassion is a skill that is typically underdeveloped in physicians.[42-43] When I asked Joon, the pain expert we met earlier in this chapter, about self-compassion, he said laughingly, "I am definitely not an expert in that!"

I asked him to imagine what would be different in his new leadership role if he could be kinder and more patient with himself. For the first time, his face softened and there was almost a twinkle in his eye as he told me, "Everything would be different, Gail, *everything*. I'd be able to relax. I wouldn't think about myself as a has-been. I didn't do all this work for 30 years for nothing. I'm really good at what I do. And if I wasn't so caught up in all these judgments of myself, I'd have more to give to my people."

Looking at Joon and Ayesha, we can see the power self-compassion has to strengthen our ability to lead, and to help us be the *Mindful MD* healing force most of us pride ourselves in being.

MINDFULNESS EXERCISE: LOVING-KINDNESS MEDITATION

As you build your mindfulness muscle by observing your thoughts and exploring a new viewpoint on pain and suffering, you'll likely begin to notice all your own inner critical voices. We all experience these, whether we are physicians or not.

To help you replace judgment with compassion, both for yourself and for others, try the loving-kindness meditation:

1. Sit comfortably with your eyes gently closed. Take three slow, deep breaths, relaxing areas of tension in your body with each exhalation. Bring your attention inward, leaving the busyness and worries of your day behind. Take some time to allow your mind to clear.

2. When your mind is quiet, bring to mind a person, or even a pet, that you feel close to. Imagine them standing in front of you. Take in the loving look in their eyes and smile. Mentally recite these words (you can read them off the page until you've committed them to memory):

May you be happy.
May you be healthy in body and mind.
May you be safe from inner and outer danger.
May you live with ease.

3. Now think of a casual acquaintance, someone toward whom you have neither positive nor negative feelings. You and this person are alike in your wish to have calm, resilience, and well-being. Mentally recite these words:

> *May you be happy.*
> *May you be healthy in body and mind.*
> *May you be safe from inner and outer danger.*
> *May you live with ease.*

4. Now bring to mind someone you have difficulty with. It could be a coworker, neighbor, family member, friend, or anyone else. You and this person are also alike in your wish to have calm, resilience, and well-being. Even if you don't fully believe them, mentally recite these words:

> *May you be happy.*
> *May you be healthy in body and mind.*
> *May you be safe from inner and outer danger.*
> *May you live with ease.*

5. Now imagine sending these same warm wishes to yourself:

> *May I be happy.*
> *May I be healthy in body and mind.*
> *May I be safe from inner and outer danger.*
> *May I live with ease.*

You can imagine sending these same warm wishes to everyone in your community or hospital, or even everyone on earth.

6. Take another three deep breaths.

When you're ready, open your eyes. Take a moment to check in with yourself and notice your state of mind after this meditation. It may be subtle, but you'll likely experience greater calm and compassion. I encourage you to continue this meditation on a regular basis.

Q AND A

1. If I'm not doing well at something, why on earth would being kind to myself motivate me?

It's a fascinating paradox, but modern motivational science informs the fact that self-kindness is much more motivating than self-bullying. You can try this out yourself right now by bringing to mind a task you need to get done but have been putting off doing.

In the first part of this exercise, tell yourself all the ways you're not good at this sort of task, how others are much better at it, and maybe that it's hopeless for you to even try.

Now, rate your level of motivation to get the task done: 0 is no motivation and 10 is "let me at it!"

Next, with the same task in mind, tell yourself all the ways you're great at this sort of task, that you're much better at it than others, and that you know that you can get it done.

Now, re-rate your motivation on the same scale.

I've done this exercise with many people, and it is a rare person whose number doesn't go up, sometimes quite significantly. There's the proof!

2. I've tried the loving-kindness meditation, and it didn't change anything—for me or for the person I'm having difficulty with. What should I do?

For most of us who have loud inner critics, building our muscle of self-kindness takes time. As with Ayesha, it can feel artificial and as if we're just saying the words without any deep feeling. I suspect that this is an experience that will resonate with many readers. When you're saying the loving-kindness meditation words directed toward yourself, one strategy is to imagine saying them toward yourself and someone you care deeply about at the same time. This can help lessen the tendency to think others deserve compassion and we, somehow, do not.

Whatever you experience, I encourage you to keep at it. The inner critic has built itself a nice home between our ears, and it can take time and patience to usher it out. I can almost guarantee that, over time, your level of compassion toward yourself will increase.

3. Isn't self-compassion selfish and self-absorbed?

This is a common misconception. It's interesting that we can spend all this time allowing our inner critic to berate us and not see just how self-absorbed this can be. What is more selfish: Giving ourselves praise and compassion so we have more energy to tend to our patients and loved ones? Or allowing the inner critic to beat us down and letting that negativity extend to those around us?

At the same time, there is a growing body of research on self-compassion* that shows self-compassionate people tend to be more caring and supporting of others, not less. Studies also demonstrate that those higher in self-compassion are better able to cope with difficulties like divorce, trauma, or chronic pain than others. I encourage you to take a look and see for yourself.

---

* - www.selfcompassion.org

5. WORK WITH WHAT IS

"It's not what happens in life that bothers us.
It's what we're believing about it that bothers us."
—Byron Katie

Lila, a 49-year-old pediatrician, found herself stewing much of the time, experiencing so much anger toward her practice manager, Joanie, that her clenched jaw made her wonder if she was developing TMJ.

A year prior, one of her partners had retired, and recently, another had developed long COVID and was out on extended leave. Recruitment efforts were in place but thus far had borne no fruit.

There were now only four of them doing the work of six. However, the patients still needed to be seen, and the understaffing meant that her schedule was frequently overbooked. Lila was willing to be flexible to accommodate the increased patient demand, but despite asking Joanie to rearrange her schedule to make it more manageable, nothing had been done. Lila railed in frustration and anger every night over dinner with her husband, a nurse at a nearby hospital. Her anger would fuel his, and their moods would both go downward together.

Lila felt a growing sense of acrimony toward Joanie. She found herself thinking, *If she's not going to help me, then why should I be nice to her?* When she'd pass Joanie in the hall, she wouldn't make eye contact, wouldn't say hello, and would barely acknowledged her presence.

Unfortunately, Lila's anger was not getting Joanie to do anything differently, and it was not improving her schedule. In fact, Joanie was starting to become spiteful in her own right. The more Lila iced her out, the less sympathetic Joanie became. When working on the department schedule, now Joanie went out of her way to discount Lila's requests.

But here Lila was, spinning and spiraling in a direction that did little besides cause her greater distress. While she enjoyed both her patients and her colleagues, she felt so much hostility toward Joanie that she began looking for a new job. Her frustration was impacting everything about her work; she actually told her husband that there was no way she could be happy if she had to continue working with Joanie.

I'll Be Happy When

Reading about Lila, you likely noticed how much she let a bothersome coworker impact her mental state.

Granted, it is challenging having a coworker you have difficulty getting along with, let alone someone who controls your work schedule. At the same time, we can mindfully recognize that conflict with people we have to interact with regularly, or who have power over us, is an aspect of nearly all our lives.

What we see, however, is that instead of becoming *more* resourceful in dealing with Joanie, it was Lila's very actions that were making things worse. Grinding her teeth and acting out with Joanie was only leading Joanie to react in kind. It was challenging enough having four physicians doing the work of six, but Lila's mounting standoff with Joanie was digging her into a deeper and deeper ditch of discontent. Unknowingly, Lila had given over much of her contentment and power to someone she didn't even like.

This begs the question: Is our happiness and contentment dependent on others and how they treat us? Do others truly have the power to determine our moods? Conversely, can we step out of this way of viewing our interactions and take that power into our own hands?

Certainly, for some, their sense of happiness or contentment derives from within themselves. They can see their strong points and successes, smile in the face of difficulty, and find ways to buoy themselves up even when the chips are down. For others, however, there can be a belief that something external to themselves is required to achieve a fulfilled state.

As physicians experience the many challenges of a healthcare system in distress, they can suffer from what I call the "I'll Be Happy When" (IBHW) disease, which is characterized by fixed views about what will permit happiness and what will not.

The IBHW disease can strike anyone at any age, but I have seen physicians have a particular propensity for it. Interestingly, when I ask groups of physicians about happiness and satisfaction in their work, I hear fairly stereotypical responses:

I'll be happy when...

> *...they get rid of this miserable electronic health record.*
>
> *...they leave me alone to see my patients.*
>
> *...my administrator listens to my concerns (in the case of Lila).*
>
> *...I finally retire.*

I also hear the converse (a variant of IBHW disease):

I can't be happy...

> *...if they don't get me a better electronic health record.*
>
> *...with all these nonphysician administrators dictating the practice of medicine.*
>
> *...given all the autonomy they have taken away.*

I've heard these IBHWs even before a career as a physician begins:

I'll be happy when...

> *...I get into medical school.*
>
> *...I match into the right residency.*
>
> *...I finish my residency and become a full-fledged attending.*

Of course, this is not limited to doctors. Non-physicians may find themselves experiencing something similar:

I'll be happy when...

> *...my son gets into a good college.*
>
> *...my spouse shows me more affection.*
>
> *...I lose 15 pounds and can fit into my old clothes.*

Think for a moment about times when you may have fallen into this very same pattern. Consider, for example, something you have been looking forward to yourself. Perhaps you've been struggling to manage the demands of your work and are telling yourself, *I can't wait to go on my vacation. I'll be so happy once I'm there.* You find yourself imagining how blissfully happy you'll be, lying carefree on the beach sipping a mimosa while your kids happily build castles in the sand. But once there, the weather is poor, the mosquitoes are out, your youngest has tantrums, and your mind is so absorbed with work that you can't actually unwind and enjoy the trip.

As this example illustrates, we can be focused on an imagined ideal, sure that it is exactly *this* thing that will bring us happiness, but sometimes (read: most times) things don't turn out quite the way we plan. Or we may reach the imagined ideal, only to feel dissatisfied and have our mind establishing a new guidepost that we believe will deliver the missing happiness. In truth, we can't ever truly know what the future will bring, and we can't know whether what our mind is telling us will make us happy will truly do so.

It's a form of mindlessness we can all get caught in, where the mind is off in stories, predictions, assumptions, and beliefs, keeping us from appreciating what is right in front of us. It's like we're wearing a mental straitjacket, imprisoning us from experiencing and fully living and enjoying the moments of our lives, here and now.

Additionally, as was the case for Lila, we can believe that we can't be happy due to a person or circumstance and that we need conditions to be a certain way to be happy and thrive. Our mind is basically telling us that things are not quite right the way they are; we need something to change for us to be okay with it. As physicians, moreover, we're used to being the expert and being in charge. But the fact of the matter is, we can only control so much.

If you stop and think about it, however, this is a fixed way of living. We tell ourselves that we can only be happy if things are different than they are. Yet, when we believe that things must be a certain way and they are not, we set ourselves up for disappointment. Whether it's a challenging practice manager, all the changes occurring in healthcare, or the weather on a rainy day, we can find ourselves turning over our sense of satisfaction to something we have little control over.

Unfortunately, these types of beliefs, just like our thoughts, stories, and patterns of reactivity, powerfully and mindlessly color our view of ourselves and our circumstances. So sure that we can't be content with things just as they are, we get lost in wishful thinking of all kinds. We delude ourselves into believing that contentment is just beyond our grasp—that if this one thing changes, somehow, our contentment will be secured. Like a dog chasing its own tail, we never seem to have a firm grip on our elusive, imagined future.

With mindfulness, we are cultivating the ability to be present and satisfied here and now, in the moments that are actually occurring in our lives.

Burnout and Learned Helplessness

When we believe that things "should" be under our control and they are not, we experience what is called learned helplessness. This is a construct that probably rings bells from your undergraduate psychology courses. In the typical experiment, rats are put in two groups and subjected to painful electric shocks. Group 1 rats are left with a lever that stops their shocks, while Group 2 rats are left with a dummy lever that does nothing. Thus, the Group 1 rats have some control over the painful stimuli, whereas the ones in Group 2 do not.

In the second phase of the experiment, a shuttle-box apparatus is utilized, in which the rats can escape electric shocks by jumping over a low partition. Group 1 rats quickly jump out of harm's way, whereas those in Group 2 make no attempts to escape; instead, they simply lie down and whine, displaying signs associated with clinical depression.[1-2]

The experience of these unfortunate rats taught the researchers that when one lacks control over their circumstances (or *believes* they lack control), one falls into learned helplessness, thinking that there is no point in trying to escape the painful stimulus. Interestingly, similar studies, in which people were exposed to inescapable noise or faced with an insoluble problem, have demonstrated that human beings are no less susceptible to learned helplessness than are research rats.[3]

Sadly, physicians in the current healthcare environment demonstrate learned helplessness in the same vein: We can succumb to the belief that something external to ourselves and outside of our control is required to free us from our current inner state.[4-5] We can be annoyed and lapse into resistance when something like mindfulness as a means of helping us is suggested. By suffering from the IBHW disease and hinging our happiness on external conditions, we are taking our happiness out of our own hands and passing it over to a magic panacea that does not actually exist.

In many ways, we are handing over our happiness and satisfaction with our careers to a broken and dysfunctional healthcare system.

Just like the rats, we give up.

Taking Back Control

We physicians have a choice.

We can hand over our happiness to a broken healthcare system, or we can take it into our own hands.

Working with what is (and not the fiction our mind creates) is the fifth way mindfulness restores our autonomy and decreases burnout. There is what we think reality should be—and there is the reality we actually have right in front of us. Like it or not, the latter is the only place where change can occur.

After all, there is a prevailing view that it is up to the healthcare system to figure itself out and correct the many problems that contribute to physician discontent. When I discuss the ways mindfulness decreases burnout with colleagues, there is often a vehement response: *Aren't you asking me to take responsibility for my happiness when it is the system that needs to change?*

My (equally) vehement response is, first off: "Of course the system needs to change! But when is that change likely to happen? By next week or even next year?" At which point, the eye-rolling when I utter the word "mindfulness" is replaced by the eye-rolling of acknowledgment that the problems in healthcare aren't going away anytime soon and that the changes needed are not ones that are a priority for industry, insurance companies, and governments that, sadly, are the ones who rule the healthcare roost. In fact, these faults mirror broader societal deficiencies that are exhibited in many other fields.

The next question I pose is this: "Do you really want to throw in the towel after all you have sacrificed to get here, and given how rich and rewarding (not to mention financially so) taking care of patients is?"

The fact of the matter is, there are deep flaws with the system. But you've invested over a decade of your life and close to a half a million dollars in education in a potentially wonderful career that requires you to be a part of it. Because that system isn't changing anytime soon, the best step you can take to preserving your career is changing the way you react to it.

As a coach, I want *all* physicians to be as resourceful as they can possibly be in effecting the type of changes in healthcare we all want to occur. As we saw with Lila, however, she was so caught in a pattern of reactivity that she was acting in ways that only served to worsen the very problem she was hoping to solve. These ways depleted her already low energy reserves (taxed by understaffing) and kept her from finding a workable solution to the scheduling problem she faced.

It's important to state that **mindful acceptance of a difficulty does not in any way mean liking the difficulty or passively resigning yourself to it**.

Quite the opposite: It simply means seeing the difficulty for what it is.

Without all the mental overlay, we gain clarity about whatever is occurring. By seeing the reality of a situation for what it is, we also begin to see ways our own actions are contributing to our difficulty. This then helps us see that we have a choice in how we respond. The clarity from mindful awareness helps us begin to take greater responsibility for creating the outcome we wish to have.

Doing so makes us *more* able to work with our difficulties, not less. After all, when we argue with reality, guess who will always lose?

Seeing this more clearly provides a powerful shift.

It is a shift from a fixed to a growth approach, and it can shift us from helplessness to true empowerment.

Don't Wait

A core part of this shift away from helplessness is deciding to grasp happiness today and not in a conditional future moment. Because we don't know what the future will hold. Tina, a 58-year-old internist, found this out the hard way.

I met Tina when she sought coaching to help with the loss of her sense of purpose. Someone who was formerly full of zest for life, she was now distraught, confused, and deeply frustrated with the practice of medicine. She shared how much she had always enjoyed her work, but with all the challenges and changes in her practice, her patience for patients was now running thin. She was frustrated with her practice manager, who in her eyes was difficult to deal with, a number cruncher, and not devoted to patients the way Tina was.

Resentful of all the changes in the practice of medicine, Tina complained to colleagues about how difficult it had all become. It was as if all her former positivity had been sucked out of her. She couldn't see anything that was going well and was all too ready to tell others how much she was looking forward to retirement.

She was exhausted by it all. She felt run-down and assumed this was due to her sense of despair about her career. She was fixed on her identity as a physician, the frustrations of practicing medicine, and her disappointments around that. Her daughter pushed Tina to see her doctor, but Tina ignored the advice. When she finally went, labs revealed that she was severely anemic. Further testing found a mass on her left kidney, and, worse still, a mass in her lung and two more in her brain.

Just like that, Tina's entire life trajectory shifted. Suddenly facing her own mortality, she was full of regrets. *Why did I waste so much time complaining? Why couldn't I have appreciated my career more? I see now that I had so much to be grateful for.*

Wishing she could go back in time and do things differently. Wishing she hadn't waited.

Tina learned the hard way the key life lesson of how rapidly life can change. Life is never stagnant, after all, and we can easily lose something that we previously took for granted—like our health or that of a loved one.

At the end of the day, wanting things to be different than they are (and banking on their magically changing) is a recipe for disappointment. We can be lost in a fantasy belief about what we think it is that will secure our satisfaction and fulfillment. Living in the antithesis of mindfulness—mindfulness being the awareness where we can see and be with things as they are—we find ourselves unable to accept what is. We get lost in a habit of hoping, striving, and grasping for things we believe will bring us the contentment we are missing. This pattern is the perfect breeding ground for burnout. And we can never actually be sure that we'll be happy when these external conditions change and our perceived prerequisites for happiness actually materialize.

Furthermore, as soon as we attain one of these prerequisites, we may find ourselves rapidly establishing another. *Okay, now I've got this thing, but if only I have that other one, then I'll be happy.*

Letting go of our IBHWs helps us recognize that while there will always be vicissitudes in our lives and work, we can maintain inner peace and happiness regardless of external conditions.

True Power

Instead of waiting and giving external conditions empowerment over our quality of work and life, perhaps our true power resides within us. Perhaps it has actually resided within us all along.

There are so many difficulties in healthcare. So many sick people. So many limits on resources. Corporatization of pharmacies, costs of health insurance and healthcare, lack of transparency about costs for medical procedures. Inefficient, burdensome authorization processes, vaccine hesitancy, and a myriad of societal problems that the physician has no ability to solve. So much inequity. So much substance use, violence, and tragedy.

With so many challenges, as individuals we can feel at the mercy of a dysfunctional system. We can feel powerless to effect change, almost like a cog in a wheel that spins wildly regardless of what we do. We can feel robbed of our autonomy. It is just this sense of lost autonomy that fuels much of the epidemic of healthcare burnout. Interestingly, it is also this sense of disempowerment that contributes to patients not following through with the lifestyle and exercise recommendations we so often prescribe.

But true power comes from within.

In his 2005 book, *The Art of Power*, Vietnamese monk, mindfulness teacher, and peace activist Thich Nhat Hanh talks about this very thing.[6] In Western society, he explains, we are taught many things about power—that powerful people are the ones with money, political station, and social connections. They are the ones in high positions. They are the ones who rule countries, Fortune 500 corporations, medical centers, hospitals, and health systems. They are celebrities, elite athletes, the talented, and the beautiful and handsome according to societal standards. They are the ones with social capital, large social media followings, and wealth. Those are the markers we use when we think about power.

For all these individuals, there is some external title or credential, formal or informal, that has granted them power. This power is real and legitimate, and I don't want to discount that. At the same time, however, we've all read news stories about deeply insecure, spiritually weak, unhappy people with plenty of this "granted power."

As *Mindful MDs*, our aspiration is to cultivate real inner power—power that resides in our ability and commitment to heal others and is neither based on a credential nor threatened or discouraged by other powerful individuals. This starts with the realization that we can cultivate power internally, through our choice of response.

Moreover, when we believe that power resides in something external to us, we create a zero-sum game, and we don't always delegate power or agency wisely. Worse, we don't effectively use the power that we *do* have. Like Lila, we act in ways that actually dissipate our power.

The quality of healthcare is dependent on a complex web of people and roles that interact and impact the other stakeholders. To say that it takes a village to keep the population of our countries in good health would be a vast underestimation of the truth.

Let's look at a real-life example of this.

Dimitri, a 60-year-old gynecologist, found his true power after being diagnosed with hypertension and early coronary heart disease. He found himself worrying about all his anger and frustration over the challenging ways his practice was running and how this might cause his blood pressure to rise and lead to a heart attack. His father had died of a heart attack when Dimitri was in medical school, around Dimitri's current age, and it weighed on him heavily, especially since his recent diagnoses.

Dimitri had been in his practice for 26 years. He had joined it from residency and had devoted his professional career to building it into the large, successful group practice it had become. But 3 years earlier, his practice had been bought by a larger health system. To contain costs, the system had downsized, and his office manager, a trusted colleague with whom Dimitri had worked for 12 years, had been let go. Now he was informed in a brief and sterile email (sound familiar?) that this health system was undergoing yet another merger—this time with the other large practice in town. It felt maddening.

Dimitri was frustrated by all the change. He'd been sent to coaching after yet another difficulty arose with his medical assistant. While he was known for his expertise and efficiency, he was also known for his temper. He didn't like it when things threw off his schedule, and all his staff knew it.

Dimitri had experienced a bad morning where he was running behind, with a number of complicated patients on his schedule. Further, he had a medical student shadowing him in his clinic, which he enjoyed, but it slowed him down and impacted his schedule.

Right after lunch, he was with a patient who was going into excessive detail about the food and lack of nursing attention she'd received during her recent hospitalization for congestive heart failure. Dimitri was feeling stressed, and when his medical assistant knocked on the door and meekly told him that his next patient was threatening to leave if Dimitri didn't see her in the next 5 minutes, Dimitri could feel his blood pressure shoot up. Normally, he would have snapped at the medical assistant—or worse. That's what he had done for years now, and that was what everyone had come to expect of him.

But Dimitri had started meditating a few months earlier. Though initially skeptical, he had reluctantly started with 5 minutes a day and early on found that it helped settle him for the workday. He was now meditating 15 minutes every morning and recommending it to many of his patients. He had also incorporated purposeful pauses, taking these when he noticed his emotional temperature rising. As a result of these mindfulness activities, he was now much more aware when he was heading into danger and was able to course-correct much of the time.

He told me how he was able to apply these mindfulness tools: "First, I was able to see what was happening. I literally told myself, 'Here I go again. My emotional temperature is rising. I need to slow myself down.' Then I paused and pushed myself to take three slow, deep breaths. That allowed me to recalibrate myself."

The pause created the critically important gap that allowed Dimitri to become the observer of himself. From that stance, he could look at the situation from a more holistic perspective, which allowed him greater flexibility, choice, and compassion in his actions.

In the past, the same situation would have pushed a button and set off a whole cascade of emotions and counterproductive actions and words. Now he had tools to help it lose its charge and stay out of, as he put it, "the same old spin of misery." Instead, he now saw that he could make mindful clinical and leadership decisions that decreased not only his misery but that of others as well.

"I am now much more able to appreciate the suffering of others. I could see that the MA is struggling too. She really must have drawn the short straw to have been the one who had to knock on my door," he chuckled. "And with patients, I used to say to them, 'Why don't you follow through with what I've instructed?' Now I see that I don't always follow through myself. My own experience with my blood pressure and heart disease has made me much more compassionate and empathetic with my patients."

Dimitri was beginning to see that while all the changes in his practice took away a level of control, he could still exercise autonomy over how he responded to the events of his days.

He was able to see the true power that resided within him to shape his responses.

In fact, with the clarity we develop through mindfulness, we begin to understand that true power comes from self-mastery, from getting to know and working with the strengths and challenges of our internal ways of being. Whatever power is stripped away by virtue of changing external circumstances, we never lose the true power that resides within.

This is the power that all the change and difficulty in healthcare cannot excise. Awareness of where our true power lies means that we can mindfully modulate the lens through which we view our experience.

When we live mindlessly, our lives are like runaway trains. The train has no working brakes, so it just goes and goes and goes. We are carried away by judgments, comparisons, worries, and fears. We are lost in thought, our minds preoccupied with all the stories the mind is so expert at creating. Drifting aimlessly from past to future and back, we are far away from that which is actually right in front of us. Even when we stop our physical motion, our mind is still on the go, careening dangerously, liable to come off the rails at any time. That is the autopilot mode that we can easily find ourselves living in.

The heavy workloads and unrealistic demands of modern living can keep us in constant motion. This is even more true in healthcare, with all the demands and inherently high stakes caring for others entails. But when this physical motion is matched with perpetual mental motion, it's a perfect setup for burnout.

The fact that physicians get caught in this mental motion makes sense: We are the product of training that keeps us rigidly stuck in the mode of always doing, always moving, and never stopping to pause, reflect, and just be. We don't learn how to pace ourselves so we can run the marathon of our careers without falling by the wayside. The ceaseless activity of the mind leaves us trapped in perpetual motion, exhausted, and burned out.

What you have seen is that we can reverse this pattern with a mindful approach to both our lives and our careers.

With this, we develop the true power that comes from having inner peace, inner stability, and inner calm. From this secure center, we also have greater compassion for ourselves and for others. This stability derives from an awareness of our inner workings: Our thoughts, beliefs, and values. With this awareness, we see through the cloud generated by our thoughts and assumptions, and we see the ever-changing nature of our thoughts and emotions. We begin to understand that we have autonomy within each and every one of us. We see that while there is a great deal that we cannot control, we can truly control the direction our mind takes us.

We also see that we have the ability to inspire others. That by making lasting change in our own lives, we can motivate those around us to do the same. That we can positively impact our healthcare system simply by showing up and being the best version of ourselves each day.

Similarly, true power comes from seeing the choice we have in how we respond to whatever difficulties arise. In the famous words attributed to Viktor Frankl, "Between stimulus and response there is a space. In that space is our power to choose our response. In our response lies our growth and our freedom."

In addition to our growth and freedom, in our response lies our power.

Mindfulness and Self-Determination

You are likely aware that one of the most common physician out-cries about all the changes in healthcare is that autonomy has been wrested from us.

I would be the last to argue that a great deal of external auton-omy has been shifted away from physicians.

At the same time, true **internal** autonomy is something a broken healthcare system cannot take from us—that is, unless we allow it to do so.

In Dr. Christina Maslach's original research (she first coined the term "burnout" in the 1970s), it was loss of autonomy and control that was an important factor in burnout. When physi-cians feel powerless, we can succumb to learned helplessness, which then serves to fuel burnout. In the context of Dr. Maslach's research, however, this loss of autonomy was largely external, and coincided with increased privatization of medicine. What was not accounted for was the other key part of the equation: The *internal* autonomy that mindfulness can restore.

Importantly, this ties into one of the most well-known and respected theories of human motivation and growth: The self-de-termination theory. This well-evidenced theory states that when three factors are present—autonomy, competency, and related-ness—human beings are motivated to achieve and successfully pursue their goals. Richard Ryan and Edward Deci, the two indi-viduals who developed the theory of self-determination, have written extensively about the connection between mindfulness and autonomy.

As opposed to the external autonomy that so many of the changes in healthcare have eroded, Drs. Ryan and Deci help us see that mindfulness actually fosters *true* autonomy. While there is no doubt that much of the external control physicians once had is no longer present, it is our true autonomy, that inner state, that has been untouched. It is this *inner* autonomy that is key to reducing burnout and reclaiming humanity in healthcare.[7-9]

We can facilitate this type of autonomy and help everyone in healthcare be less susceptible to reactivity, undue stress, and suffering. "Being mindful of the present, free of defenses and judgments, allows information to flow and for what is pertinent to become clearer and more salient. Put another way, mindfulness precipitates less ego involvement, reactivity, and attachment to phenomena, and this allows for more deeply valued, authentic responses."[10]

When we as physicians step out of our conditioning—our identity as special and our training-instilled beliefs around perfection, invulnerability, and the ability to control that which is often beyond our control—we can move from these extrinsic motivators to those more aligned with who we truly are, and who we were when we decided to enter the profession of medicine in the first place.

Doing so brings us back to what is most deeply important to us.

The Superpower of Mindfulness

Mindfulness provides exactly what we need to free ourselves from the trap of never-ending pressure and ever-increasing demands that keep us running, running, running. We can find the peace and happiness that we seek in every moment of our lives. We can inhabit this moment, the only moment that is actually real, with greater intentionality. We can build our ability to work productively with what is. In doing so, we can be steady and create steadiness, for ourselves and for those around us. We can be the true leader in our own lives, in our workplaces, and in the world around us.

When we become the master of our own minds, we develop more than power. We develop a kind of superpower. In the midst of all the chaos and dysfunction around us, we can smile and laugh, enjoy the career we've worked so hard for, and live great lives. We can let go of everything that we can't control and feel real confidence and power in what we can. This is what mindfulness affords us.

Reading this, you may be wondering: *Is it easy to develop this superpower? Is this really something we can do?*

It isn't easy—but neither was your medical training, and neither is living life burned out. Yet, it's something we can all achieve, with enough patience, persistence, and (mindful) effort. In many ways it is simple, but not easy. It takes effort—and lots of it.

Becoming a *Mindful MD* means making changes. It means learning to let go of ways of being that do not serve our broader purpose. Stepping out of all the judgments the mind is always ready to make. Accepting that life is full of challenges and trusting that you have what you need to meet them. Being kind and patient with yourself.

While this is true, however, you do not need to do it all at once. Every time you make one small, incremental mindful change, you come closer and closer to a more authentic and easeful life, a reduction in suffering, and an increase in positivity and autonomy.

This superpower also takes a willingness to start over, to put aside our expertise around what we believe we know and think we understand, and to adopt the mindset of one who doesn't know. It takes a willingness to be a beginner. This may be challenging for the highly educated physician who has been taught that they are the expert, yet this mindset is wise, affirming, and powerful. This mindset is the one that characterizes true knowing, true leadership, and true power.

With practice, a more mindful life is possible. It is, however, a journey in the direction of a destination. Go in the direction of your intention for change, and you will feel better and better bit by bit. By letting go of any expectation of perfection, you can do this incrementally, and with compassion for yourself and for others.

Just as overall improvement to the healthcare system will not happen overnight, with each amount of positive effort, self-compassion, and the willingness to practice, each of us can continue to build our capacity to live and work mindfully. Each of us can help shift the healthcare system in the direction of our vision, one step at a time.

Physician training leaves the typical doctor wary of criticism, of being told that we aren't good enough, and of living in a small and fearful state. This subdues our natural goodwill, curiosity, and openness to others. It contributes to our putting up a wall to shield ourselves from judgment and blame.

And yet, these are qualities we can reclaim.

We can allow the power of compassion and human connection to redirect us to what is truly important. We can pay attention to our inner voice—the one that knows that each and every one of us has the power to live with equanimity and fulfillment.

As *Mindful MDs*, we can be happy today, not with what we wish healthcare was like, but with what is.

MINDFULNESS EXERCISE: SETTING YOUR INTENTION

As you have learned, our minds are expert at fixed IBHW type of thoughts, stories, and beliefs. Given the autopilot many of us experience, we are not typically fully conscious of how things are impacting us or how we are responding to people and events. We can find ourselves almost blown about by the exigencies of the day.

To better work with the reality of what is, setting an intention is a powerful way to right this tendency toward autopilot, taking us out of often unseen yet fixed views and beliefs, and helping us work with what is.

Unlike New Year's resolutions, which tend to be black-and-white and leave us feeling like we've either succeeded or failed, intentions work because they simply set a direction we wish to follow. They serve to direct our energy and attention toward what we want. In a sense, they provide a pragmatic North Star for our efforts.

To begin, answer these questions:

How do I want to be showing up?

What is one thing I'd like to be doing more of?

_____

_____

_____

_____

Next, ask yourself:

At the end of my day, what do I want to look back and see?

What will allow me to leave work today with my head held high?

_____

_____

_____

_____

Last, write down one intention for your day.

_____

_____

_____

Be sure to look at your intention as you progress in your day.

At the end of the day, review the intention you set and consider whether your actions aligned with your intention. Try not to judge yourself if you go astray. Tomorrow always represents another opportunity.

Remember, there is no success or failure, only support for you to be fully mindful in how you show up.

Q AND A

1. As a physician, I don't feel like I have any power anymore. It feels like it's all been taken from me. What can I do?

Many physicians (and others in healthcare) have this very same view. There is no question that you may not have the decision-making power to control all the factors that contribute to how your practice runs. That is the external autonomy that, for many physicians, has most definitely been lessened. The shift toward corporate control in healthcare has been a powerful force.

At the same time, what I am getting at in this book, and what I encourage you to sit with, is that this doesn't mean you have no power. As with the studies on rats, believing that we are powerless is a fast path to learned helplessness. Learned helplessness, not surprisingly, predisposes us to burnout.

While you may no longer have the power to control these external factors, take heart as I quote Victor Frankl once again, a man who survived unspeakable horrors in a Nazi concentration camp: "Everything can be taken from a man but one thing: the last of the human freedoms—to choose one's attitude in any given set of circumstances, to choose one's own way."

What can never be taken from you is your true autonomy.

That is what mindfulness helps you regain.

2. I can see how mindfulness could be the superpower you claim it is. But I've been meditating for a month now, and I can still be pretty reactive with my wife and kids. I don't feel confident in myself; are you sure I can develop this?

Yes! You can definitely develop the superpower of mindfulness. Following the 6 ways this book provides is your roadmap for doing so. But you'll have to be patient with yourself, as it will take time. Just like building muscles at the gym, it won't occur overnight. It will take many reps and a lot of practice. Just like the physicians you're reading about in this book, however, you'll be building your new skills and the forward momentum that will most definitely get you where you want to go.

Be patient and keep trying. Our progress is not linear; there will be setbacks and times where you feel like you haven't made progress. But as you measure in months and weeks and not days, you'll see how far you've come.

3. Like Tina, I waited. Unfortunately, then my husband got into a bad car accident and now is in a rehab for a broken pelvis, arm, and leg, and a severe concussion. Now I see just how much I was putting off really living and enjoying my life and career as a physician. I'm writing in to reinforce what you're saying, as we just never know what's coming around the next corner.

Oh my goodness, how awful. My heart really goes out to your husband, and to you.

I am saddened that you've had to find out the hard way just how impermanent things can be. The good news is you can be present and compassionate in the face of this hardship, and choose to live **here and now.**

Thank you for sharing this. I know that others can learn from your experience.

6. CULTIVATE UPWARD SPIRALS

"Once you leave the ground, you fly. Some people fly longer than others."
—Michael Jordan

O veruse of the problem-focused lens, combined with the brain's negativity bias, keeps many physicians focused on what's going wrong as opposed to what is going well, leaving us depleted and unfulfilled, a setup for burnout. Without taking in the sustenance that positive experiences provide, this tunnel vision traps us in downward spirals of annoyance, frustration, and lack of satisfaction with our work. But when we replace these negative patterns with a focus on compassion, purpose, and positive self-talk, we quickly find greater energy, emotion, and fulfillment than we could possibly imagine.

After all, I know that you picked up this book for a reason.

After spending several chapters discussing burnout and the negative patterns that keep us there, I'm sure you're quite ready to hear about what is on the other side. Fortunately, there is a great deal that greets us. Let's take a look at what life can look like as a physician when you move past burnout and into the sixth way that mindfulness restores autonomy and cures burnout: Cultivating the upward spirals that are well within your reach.

Up or Down?

Imagine that you head off to work, get caught in traffic, and feel frustrated that there are so many cars on the road. You observe that your emotional temperature has risen, and you take a purposeful pause, stopping and taking a few deep breaths. You cool down and are able to enjoy the beautiful spring colors you pass on your commute.

You get to work, and your medical assistant is late getting your first patient into the exam room. You are worried about running late, and then see that they haven't recorded the patient's vital signs as they have been instructed. You find yourself quite annoyed by this, with second arrows pinging around you. Knowing that you're at risk of being impatient (or worse), you realize you have a choice. You can let this impact your mood, or you can take a moment to regroup before going in to see the patient. You do the latter, exercising true power, and you're able to focus on the patient's concerns and have a pleasant and productive interaction. You leave the visit feeling good about it, dictate and close your note, and move on to the next patient.

As you go through your day, you continue to keep an eye on your internal state, meeting moments of frustration by reminding yourself that it's just the way it is, that the practice of medicine involves many stresses. You bring yourself compassion for the difficulties you face and take purposeful pauses throughout your day. When your mind drifts to a conflict you've had with your spouse or teenager, you take a breath, remind yourself how strong that relationship is, and send them a sweet text (or at least hold off on sending a not-so-sweet one).

At the noontime department meeting, your chief discusses the high rates of burnout revealed in a recent survey. You're tempted to roll your eyes and make a snarky comment about how corporate medicine is out to get us all, but you reconsider. You can see, after all, that your words and actions play a role in the culture of the department, and you want to do what you can to help. You remind yourself that being engaged helps you stay out of burnout, and so you share an idea you have about how the group can work more cohesively as a team. When you see a colleague who looks downtrodden, you share compassion through a knowing smile, and can tell that doing so gives them the energy they need to get through their day. Seeing this reenergizes you as well.

When your tenth patient of the day comes in, and they haven't lost the 15 pounds they committed to 6 months ago (and have actually put some on), you put aside a negative judgment and listen compassionately, affirming how hard it is to effect change. You remind them what's at stake for them and their family, and you witness them leaving with a new resolve. (They even come back 6 months later down 10.)

Before leaving the office, you notice yourself frustrated with the charting and paperwork you have yet to complete. You take several slow, deep breaths, acknowledging your frustration with the medical system and its bureaucracies. Noticing the second arrows, you let that emotion go, and you're able to focus well and finish your charting in a half hour, leaving time to head home and enjoy dinner with your family.

On your drive home, you mentally unpack anything lingering from the day and set the intention to let go of whatever is not serving you.

You are still tired by the end of your day, but instead of being irritable and impatient as your child tells you about their day, you both have some laughs and leave the dinner table in a good mood. As a result of getting your charting done during the workday, you only have to spend a few minutes on the computer and then can have a relaxing time with your spouse discussing weekend plans. You get into bed in a calm state and awaken feeling rested and refreshed.

Sounds like a great day, no?

Now let's zoom out and see what a month of days like this looks like. A year. An entire career. This observing and reframing. This pausing and taking care of yourself through the challenges you encounter. This knowing that you have helped buoy your colleagues up, as opposed to not doing anything for them or actively bringing them down. The letting the little things go.

Each and every one of these moment-to-moment choices you make (read: autonomy) serves to create the upward spirals that nourish your days.

A string of these upward days, in aggregate, forms the momentum and energy that build your ability to cope and thrive, and spreads positive contagion to those around you.

Slowly and gradually, you work your way out of burnout, out of self-defeating messaging and mental patterns, out of a paralyzing sense of victimhood in an f'd-up medical system (my editor held me back here). You become happier, more productive, more present at work and at home. More and more, you become your best possible self.

Now let's be real here: This is a stepwise endeavor, and you may find yourself experiencing resistance in the process. As with our patients who struggle to lose weight, stop smoking, improve their A1Cs, eat a low-sodium diet, and exercise regularly, change requires motivation, and lots of it. Utilizing the mindful steps you've learned, moving past burnout initially means moving toward, and being open to, contentment. A big step from "really bad" is "just kind of bad," after all, and another big step from there is having "just okay" days. But with persistence, patience, and mindful practice, every small step provides the positive feedback needed to motivate the next one. When on an upward spiral, the momentum needed to continue that trajectory is light-years less than trying to move up from a downward flow.

Before you know it, you have moved into a wave of momentum that is hard to stop.

This upward spiral is the complete antithesis of burnout.

Cultivating upward spirals is even something that can begin in our medical training. In fact, the 6 ways in this book provide a roadmap for preventing patterns of burnout that develop in training, planting healthy roots that foster growth toward well-being and thriving in our careers.

Now, you may be thinking: *Okay, here it comes. Another person telling me that if I put on a smile, everything will be okay. That if I just think positive thoughts, all the problems in my practice will just melt away, and I'll wander off into la-la land.*

Well, it certainly isn't as simple or as easy as just being posi-tive—but it certainly won't hurt. And my response to whether it will make everything okay is: "Yes and no."

Thinking positive thoughts will not change the traffic on your commute. It won't make your medical assistant magically start doing what they've been instructed to do. It won't change the fact that some patients and some administrators can be difficult to deal with.

But the cumulative impact of consistently reshaping how you respond to the situations you're placed in will transform your reality. Utilizing the mindfulness tools we've explored will help you gain control over whether you go in a downward or upward direction. They will help you notice when you're slipping into old patterns and give you the tools to step away from them. They will help you tap into compassion and purpose with your patients and within yourself. They will help you maintain more calm throughout your day. They will help you be far less reactive to whatever difficulties your EMR or inbox bring, thus increas-ing your efficiency in getting it all done. They will help you leave work at work and be much more present with your loved ones.

They will rebuild the autonomy you need to not just move away from burnout but to actually thrive. Detaching from the automatic, negative responses of the mind and moving toward compassion, presence, and true inner autonomy will have mas-sive impacts on how you show up to your practice.

Of course, your life outside of work will reap the benefits. You will experience more fulfilling, deeper relationships, along with greater happiness and calm at home (isn't that what we all want?). You will be able to be more of yourself and be more present and compassionate with your loved ones. And you'll have the resources to spend time and energy on your most important patient—you.

Utilizing the mindfulness strategies outlined in this book has put my own burnout far in the rearview mirror. It's helped me shed many of the patterns I adopted in training. I now spend more time in nature, eating nutritious food, exercising, and being fully present for the moments that make up my life and work. I catch my mind when the inner critic or monkey mind takes over, and I am able to question the veracity of their stories and move into mental dialogue that is productive. I am happy and I am fulfilled by my work. And although I am no longer practicing medicine, I have seen the same in almost every practicing physician I have coached.

With consistent implementation, these mindfulness tools and strategies will help you make burnout a thing of the past. They will help you access and enjoy a variety of positive emotions and experiences, ones that previously may have been buried beneath a mound of discontent. And you will feel the palpable momentum behind a real upward spiral.

Unsurprisingly, it feels good to feel good.

There is a rich body of research indicating that the benefits of upward spirals and positive emotions are real. Although the field of psychology historically focused much more on the negative (i.e., what was wrong with human beings) than on the opposite, the current focus is more of a both/and. In fact, there are now thousands of studies validating the mental health, relationship, and physical health benefits of positive emotions and upward spirals.

These are fundamental building blocks for cultivating resilience, flourishing, vitality, happiness, and life and work satisfaction.[1-4] They are nutrients that fuel optimal function in the human species. They are nutrients that mindfulness helps us develop, and they are ones that can provide just the sustenance we need to face whatever strife the healthcare system puts in our path.

It also turns out that positive emotions influence variables vital for workplace success, such as creativity, work engagement, coping, teamwork and collaboration, customer satisfaction, leadership, and job performance.[5-6]

Importantly, positive emotions provide an antidote to the negativity that comes with burnout in medical students, residents, and beyond.[7-10] Indeed, in addition to emotional fatigue, cynicism, and disconnection from our accomplishments, the anguish of burnout includes a profound downward spiral all its own, where we find ourselves trapped in a series of negative thoughts, emotions, and actions that almost continuously feed back into themselves, causing our mental state and mood to become progressively worse. Negative thoughts, rumination, and disconnection from what's going well—around and around it goes, spiraling us further and further down. We're captive to a downward spiral, and often we're not even aware that one has taken hold.

Even if we're not in burnout, given all the difficulties in healthcare, negativity abounds at every turn. Hospital cafeterias are populated with clinicians complaining about all the difficulties. Many physicians say they wouldn't recommend a career in medicine to their kids. There is almost a type of contagion toward the negative. We run into a colleague, and they complain to us about the misguided emphasis on productivity. We join in and share our complaint about how many hours we have to spend on the electronic record. As Austin, a Midwestern neurosurgeon, put it, "I don't even want to talk to my colleagues anymore. It just takes me down the drain."

It's almost as if there is a powerful vortex of negativity in healthcare, pulling us all down, down, down.

Of course, workplace cafeterias in law, business, technology, and education are likely full of the same chatter. It's normal for human beings who share experiences to lament over shared burdens. However, there's a difference between healthy venting and the ever-seductive dwelling in the negative, which may feel good in the moment, but invariably orients us toward burnout.

So what do we do?

As we saw earlier with Lila, perhaps we can have more control over our states than we typically realize.

The Seeds We Water

I'll borrow from Buddhist tradition and share a concept that shows us the power we have to mindfully move from downward to upward spirals, in a way that dramatically shifts our inner experience.

Imagine for a moment that you are the farmer of a large, open field—a very fertile field, well watered, and made up of rich earth that contains all the nutrients your plants need to flourish and grow. In this field, whatever seeds you water will grow. Whether it is turnips or tulips, wheat or watermelons, peas or petunias, the conditions are ripe, and an abundant harvest will be readily achieved.

But in your field there are also many weeds. You realize that you have a choice: Will you water healthful fruit and vegetables, or will you water the weeds? You have the option to do either one, as you are the arbiter of what grows in this fertile land.

We can think of the mind in a similar way. Our mind is a large expanse, abundant and ripe for growth. Our minds can grow many wonderful things. Although we don't always appreciate this, we are the ones who decide what will grow in the space that resides between our two ears.

Will we grow love, kindness, and compassion? Will we grow generosity to those around us? Will we grow gratitude for the many things we have in our lives?

Alternatively, will we grow anger, vengeance, meanness, and greed? Will we grow annoyance, frustration, blame, hostility, hatred, and cruelty? Will we even grow the belief that we are a victim and that we are helpless to improve our fate?

Each and every day, we have a choice over which seeds we water. If we water the seeds of anger, anxiety, irritability, meanness, and greed, these are the ones that will strengthen and grow. If we tend to see what isn't going well, find fault with others and with ourselves, and carry grudges for things large and small, those are the seeds we are watering. Over time, they are the ones that will grow tall and strong, crowding out all the others.

Yet, if you're someone who sees the good and praises yourself and others for their strengths and contributions, that is what will flourish. If you water the seeds of gratitude, generosity, kindness, and compassion, those are the ones that will grow stronger.

And by noticing when the weeds of fear and lack are clamoring for water, and calmly returning to the present, we can gradually starve them out.

As we have seen, our minds are busy places with tens of thousands of thoughts arising every day. Some are positive and productive, yet many are not. We can focus on (read: water) the seeds of positivity, or we can water the seeds of negativity. We can ignore all of the good in our lives and let those plants wither, or we can choose not to ruminate on what's going wrong, avoiding an overgrowth of unhealthy sprouts. If we water weeds, it is weeds that will grow and flourish.

While it can seem like we have little control over our thoughts, it turns out that we actually have full choice about which ones we foster—certainly much more choice than we learn in medical training.

Here's the story of one last discontented doctor (I know I have introduced you to many) and his experience with watering mental seeds.

Chris was a 56-year-old orthopedist, a physician who worked hard and prided himself on always putting his patients first. When his practice converted to an electronic record, the clerical staff were overwhelmed by the task of inputting data from paper charts into the EMR. Frustrated by not having old records at his fingertips—and as something of a perfectionist—Chris took on this responsibility himself and soon found himself saddled with work. He spent time inputting old records every day when he finished operating and seeing patients in the office.

This extra work on top of his usual responsibilities took a toll. Chris was exhausted. He felt completely put upon. At the same time, he was long frustrated when his nurses didn't follow the protocols he had established. Sadly, Chris started snapping at people. After one such incident, Chris was reported to his state physician health services. Bruce, the intake social worker, told me, "You know, Gail, this guy is really a piece of work. He's a nasty 'you-know-what,' and people don't want to work with him."

With this introduction, I braced myself for what was to come, but I actually found Chris to be a likable individual. Like many physicians sent for coaching, he initially railed against the system, the electronic record, and all the pressures that were "sucking the life out of [him]." He talked about how the EMR was ruining the practice of medicine and his sense that things were much better with the old-fashioned paper charts. He told me how his days were drudgery, spending hours upon hours on what he considered the useless activity of charting.

He continued, "Gail, I'm so miserable that, from the moment I get out of bed, I wonder how I will get through another day. My practice is miserable, the schedule is out of control, and no one is making it any better."

Chris was caught in a pattern of blaming everyone, completely focused on the negative. As he put it: "I was in a ditch of negativity. It almost seemed like everybody was out to get me."

Without realizing it, he was busy watering the weeds in his mind.

As he saw that I was on his side, however, he dropped the blame script and began to look at the part he played in his predicament. He recognized that he had slid into bad habits and felt ashamed of how negative and reactive he had become.

We reviewed a simple protocol where he paid attention to times when he was replaying the negative thought and story script. When he observed this, he was instructed to use a purposeful pause to calm himself down.

He came to our next session excited to report that he had a number of successes. He shared that when he'd notice anger, annoyance, and frustration, he would stop and take a purposeful pause. He'd take at least three deep breaths, observe his inner state, and only then proceed. From this refreshed vantage point, he was able to see that everyone in his office was working hard. In fact, for the most part, they were each trying their best to give patients what they needed and make sure the office functioned efficiently. They were also trying to help him let go of the clerical work and return to being the doctor. But the demands were many and were not letting up.

As Chris took more pauses and was able to reflect more on his situation, he saw how he had fallen prey to the negativity bias, and that he'd begun to feel victimized by the story his mind had labeled "yet another miserable day."

He also began to see that he could rewrite the script.

Chris started asking himself a few powerful questions each morning before arriving at work. In particular, he asked himself, *What do I need to do to make today a good day?* and *How can I contribute to making this a good one for others as well?*

"When I flipped the narrative from 'This day is going to be miserable' to seeing that I had some choice in what kind of day unfolded," he shared, "I just couldn't believe how much I had not seen."

He continued, "I was letting the electronic record destroy what was most important to me. How ridiculous is that? Now I'm conscious of where I'm going and why, and I can work productively with myself and others, and keep things from snowballing down in the way they were."

Chris learned that watering the seeds of negativity generated greater negativity and only served to trap him in anxiety and irritability. So instead, he worked on watering the positive. In doing so, he found that the payoff was significant. Rather than the downward spiral he had been living in, he now saw the ways he could uplift not just himself, but those he worked with as well.

Additionally, shifting to upward spirals actually helped Chris rewire his brain.

Neuroplasticity Revisited

Coming back to the concept of neuroplasticity, an emerging body of research helps us understand this important phenomenon.[11-12]

If we are people who tend to focus on the negative, it may be that we do so many times a day. Arguments, petty slights, judgments of others. What we don't like about our boss, coworker, spouse, or child. Ways we don't think we acted right, missed opportunities, or times we didn't get our way. That we don't like the weather, the stock market, or our aging body. Accusing ourselves of not being smart enough, attractive enough, or young enough in our appearance. Believing we are an imposter as opposed to the real deal.

Add up the negative thoughts many of us think every day, and we begin to see how our brain is getting a lot of practice focusing on what is going wrong instead of what is going right.

Up until just a couple of decades ago, medical students were taught that the human brain stopped growing after adolescence and that after a certain age, new neuronal connections were impossible. We now know that while neuroplasticity decreases as we age, our brains remain capable of adapting. The human brain at all ages is malleable; synaptic patterns are almost constantly being remapped. While the brain has a tendency toward the preset neuronal patterns that it's spent considerable time developing, these patterns can be retooled and unlearned.[13-16]

Moreover, the human brain includes some 100 billion neurons, and the brain possesses the remarkable capacity to reorganize pathways, create new connections, and, in some cases, even create new neurons. Numerous studies of the human brain demonstrate this phenomenon in both structure and function. You may be familiar with the adage "neurons that fire together, wire together." Much the way water flowing down a mountainside causes grooves to form on its surface, something similar happens in our brains. With repeated use, synaptic pathways form in our brains that then guide further neuronal transmission.

Furthermore, a rich and growing literature demonstrates the many ways mindfulness meditation contributes to neuroplasticity. It has been well demonstrated that meditation reduces age-related brain degeneration and improves cognitive function.[17-21] Mindfulness training is also positively correlated with improvements in attention, working memory, spatial abilities, and long-term memory.[22-25] Mindfulness meditation increases gray matter in the left hippocampus, posterior cingulate cortex, and temporoparietal junction—regions involved in learning and memory processing, emotion regulation, and perspective taking.[26] Neuroplasticity also involves shrinkage in size of the amygdala and increase in telomere length, two processes meditation has been shown to impact.[27-28]

This is wonderful news! It means that we can grow the connections that are most helpful for us. We can move from passive acceptance of patterns of negativity and grow patterns that are resourceful and sustaining. Just as Chris was developing his ability to focus on helpful mental patterns, his brain was utilizing that new information to establish new synaptic patterns, ones that, with repetition and practice, would then become his new default. The brain's ability to build new pathways is key in shifting from downward to upward spirals.

Reason to SMILE

The growing evidence base of neuroplasticity should give us reason to smile. Instead of accepting the limitations of our thought patterns, these studies help us see that we can be agents of change. Instead of blindly succumbing to our brain's bias toward the negative, we can cultivate our capacity to focus our mind on the positive. Instead of providing the fuel for burnout, we can create upward spirals that build our resilience in the face of the difficulties we face.

I have seen this phenomenon at play in almost all the physicians I have coached.

I have also seen this in myself.

You're not seeing this side of me in this book, but I have to admit that for much of my life I was someone who was very reactive and tended toward downward spirals. If something went wrong with one of my patients, I would jump to a concern over what errors I might have made. If my son got angry at me and accused me of being the worst mother of all time, I took it very personally, often spitting back something nasty in kind. When I didn't see eye to eye with my boss in hospice, my mind immediately pronounced her a foolish overlord who just couldn't see that my way was the right one.

In terms of the childhood abuse that I mentioned in the introduction, I was left with PTSD. I startled easily, awoke at night in fear, and often found myself involuntarily reliving past painful events. In many ways, this left me feeling like a marionette, at the whim of forces outside of myself instead of being the master of my own mind and life.

After much mindfulness practice, however, I am living with far greater ease. I am much more able to see what my mind is up to and intervene when unhelpful thoughts, stories, and emotions arise. I can roll with the changing circumstances of my life with much greater agility and equanimity. I can see much more clearly when I am emotionally activated, and, equally clearly, I can see the choice I have in how I respond.

I am also far more compassionate with my own foibles and failings, which has contributed to my ability to improve upon them. I have tools to hold myself steady no matter what arises. While my son and others would say that I do none of this perfectly, I suspect they would also say that I'm a heck of a lot better with them than prior to my stumble into mindfulness so many years in the past.

You see, my friends, mindfulness is all about having choice and recognizing the ability to change. It helps us have agency over ourselves and actions. It is the antidote to whatever loss of autonomy we face in our work, in healthcare and beyond.

When I think about this, I find myself smiling, so I coined an appropriately named acronym:

S: **See** *what's truly here*

M: **Meet** *it with curiosity and compassion, not judgment*

I: **Investigate** *with openness and kindness*

L: **Learn** *new ways of being*

E: **Engage** *with wisdom and equanimity*

In other words, when we step out of all our mental judgments and stories and step into mindful awareness, we can see more clearly what it is that is actually happening. Instead of standing right underneath the waterfall, we have moved a comfortable distance and can observe what's occurring without getting drenched. From this vantage point, we leave the distortions and misperceptions our minds are so prone to generating, and we see the truth of our experience.

As we drop all the judgment, there is greater room for compassion. In fact, as judgment abates, our natural human compassion blossoms. As we counter the brain's negativity bias, there is an expansiveness and equanimity that follows. That is yet another ingredient of the upward spiral.

Further, we can lean into curiosity, another word for investigation. We are open to questioning that which may have been previously blindly accepted as truth. When we investigate in an open way, the result is that we learn. We apply our natural love of learning toward ourselves and our viewpoints, as well as those of our patients.

All these processes allow us to be present with whatever we face and engage with the moments of our lives with wisdom and equanimity.

In this way, a mindful approach helps physicians develop the steadiness that is required to navigate the change and uncertainty that are likely to continue in the complex landscape of healthcare.

When we think about mindfulness this way, we shift ourselves from facing our difficulties with a scowl to facing them with a smile. This is not a false smile or a Pollyanna one. Instead, it is a smile that acknowledges that we have what we need to thrive, no matter what difficulty comes in our path.

What this means is that we don't have to give over our contentment to a healthcare system gone awry. This is one of the most important sentences in this entire book, so let me repeat it:

What this means is that we don't have to give over our contentment to a healthcare system gone awry.

You can choose to focus on what is under your control and completely reclaim your life and career, engaging in an upward spiral that previously seemed impossible. In the presence of this broken system, and in spite of it, as a *Mindful MD* you can enjoy the life and career you've worked so hard for.

MINDFULNESS EXERCISE: WATER THE SEEDS OF GREATER POSITIVITY

As we have seen, the human mind is programmed to focus on the negative. This leads us to dwell on everything that is going wrong and not what is going right. We tend to do this rather automatically, without even realizing what our mind is up to or the impact it has on us—but the impact is mighty, fueling anxiety, irritability, and narrow-mindedness. Yet, we can cultivate our ability to see the positives. We can move from the negativity bias to one of much greater positivity.

As you go through your day today:

1. Notice whether your mind is drawn to the positive or negative.

2. See if you can catch at least three negative thoughts. These might be about something that annoys or frustrates you. It could be something about a person that you don't like, or think they're doing poorly. It could be judgments about yourself.

3. Ask yourself:

- *How is this negative thought helping me?*
- *Is this negative thought causing me anguish or pain?*

4. Now ask yourself:

- *How can I water a seed of greater positivity instead?*

After doing this, see what you learn. Did you find any benefit in shifting from the negative to the positive?

If you found that this shift helped you, can you try doing it again tomorrow?

As you build this ability to water different seeds, you'll likely find yourself feeling lighter and brighter, each and every day.

Q AND A

1. I tend to be a glass-half-empty kind of person. Are you saying I can just drop that with a little meditation?

Many of us can tend toward the down, no doubt about it. The negativity bias has a powerful hold on our brains.

I'm not saying that with meditation you can just drop this. What I am saying is that you can build your ability to shift toward the positive. Extensive research on neuroplasticity shows us that we have a great deal more control over our states than most of us realize. We can train our brains to attune much more to the positives that are often less visible to us. With mindfulness, we develop the critically important awareness of when we are leaning more down than up. With this awareness, we can then see that we have a choice of going in that downward direction or not. It doesn't happen overnight (although I sure wish it did), but it definitely occurs with the repetition and practice that meditation provides.

2. I like the idea of my mind as a garden, but how can I stop watering negative seeds?

I'm glad you like this concept, as I myself have found it extremely helpful.

Unhelpful watering come in many forms. Overly negative colleagues and friends. Violent images in books, movies, or TV. Alcohol or other substance misuse. These are all common ones. Too much time on social media is another.

While we all want to be up-to-date on world events, excessive watching or reading of the news can also be a highly unhelpful seed. It can foster weeds of paranoia and fear.

It won't be the same for each of us, but what's key is mindful awareness of what it is that pulls you down or brings you up. Once you can see these more clearly, you will also rapidly see the choice you have in minimizing these unhelpful inputs. Just as Chris did, so you can too.

3. I tried your SMILE acronym, and it's already helping me see how I can meet my challenges with greater equanimity and resourcefulness. Now that I see the benefits more clearly, it's hard seeing just how mindless and judgmental others around me are. How can I get them to do the things you've taught me to do?

As we become more mindful, many individuals struggle with wanting others to do the same. I have also noticed this in myself. Applying the **SMILE** acronym in these situations and seeing what's truly here, however, I begin to **See** how I am actually the one lapsing into judgmental thinking, sitting around and judging others for not being mindful enough! I can pause and **Meet** my own tendency to form judgments with curiosity and compassion. When I **Investigate** with openness and kindness, I can **Learn** more about my own tendencies toward judgment. I can then move to **Engaging** both the other person and myself with wisdom, equanimity, and compassion, not further judgment.

After all, meeting their judgmentalism with my own typically only serves to rigidify the situation, as I become polarized in my views and beliefs.

Investigating my own mind then allows me to learn more about myself and almost automatically takes me to greater wisdom and equanimity in how I interact with them. With that, I can often find a more resourceful way to approach the entire situation.

But don't take my word for this! Try it yourself and see.

Moving Forward

We've been on quite a journey together, haven't we? If you've made it this far, you've soaked in a great deal about how mindfulness and emotional management can help us overcome burnout and regain our autonomy and power within a broken system.

I hope you are excited to make burnout a thing of the past. To move into a new way of working and living—confidently, powerfully, and with rightful autonomy. To reengage with your purpose and to bring compassion and presence to yourself and your career, and to those around you. To make sense of this crazy healthcare ecosystem and have the balance, steadiness, and calm you need to keep it from overwhelming you.

To get there, you now have tools to leave behind the mindlessness many of us learned in our training, both formal and otherwise. You have seen the ways you can train your mind to focus on the present so that you can be fully intentional in how you interpret, react, and respond to the difficulties you face. Yes, the difficulties you face in healthcare, but also well beyond.

Let's do a brief recap.

In Part I, we looked at the ways the mindset of the physician is formed. We looked at the early life of the physician, how being identified as the smart and special one begins to create a sense of identity that then makes it difficult for the physician to embrace our authentic selves.

We then looked at medical training, which, inadvertently and along with many positives, creates a mindless mindset of fear, armoring, rigidity, and imbalance. A fixed medical mindset that sets in motion patterns that silently but relentlessly set us up for burnout.

We examined the phenomenon of burnout: The state of emotional exhaustion, depletion, cynicism, and difficulty appreciating the good, both around and within us.

Then we switched the frame and took a deep dive into mindfulness and 6 ways we can use it to restore autonomy and alleviate burnout (read: get our lives back).

In the first two of these ways, we explored the fact that the human mind is an extraordinarily busy place, with thousands of thoughts a day, many of them of highly questionable utility. You learned the powerful truth that you are not your thoughts, as well as ways to create a gap between yourself and your busy mind.

We then looked at the power of mindful awareness—the ability to put aside filters and stories so that we can gain clarity around what is actually going on within and around us. We further examined ways to reduce reactivity, becoming the observer of your own mind and moving from subjective seeing to a much more objective and empowered stance.

With each of these first three ways, I challenged you to consider the ways some of your own struggles are due to the complexities of your mind.

These first three ways grew your awareness of what your mind is up to and the fact that you don't have to believe and succumb to all your thoughts, stories, and patterns of reactivity!

Next, we took a deep dive into compassion—for self and for others—and examined how it can be lost as well as how it, and your sense of purpose, can be restored.

We then moved on to working with what is, as well as the fact that without mindful acceptance we can unknowingly be the ones contributing to the very difficulties we so readily lay blame for on others, and on a highly dysfunctional healthcare system.

Last, we explored the role of positive versus negative emotions, and the ways we can cultivate the upward spirals that nourish and sustain us, helping us weather the difficulties we face.

Along the way, you heard about many physicians and the struggles they experience. You also heard about the many ways mindfulness helped them meet these struggles and reclaim the autonomy and power that is rightfully theirs.

It's your turn now.

I truly hope that this book has inspired you to become a *Mindful MD* and regain your autonomy and happiness in your career. I hope you've been able to appreciate the many ways mindfulness can restore humanity in our broken healthcare system.

You won't become mindful overnight! You've had the mental patterns you have for quite some time, and your mind has become conditioned to follow those patterns. Retraining your mind will require practice. Just like going to the gym to build skeletal muscle mass, retraining your mind will require a lot of reps. That is the purpose of the exercises that follow each chapter of this book. To become more mindful, practice them on a regular basis. In doing so, I know you will build your mindful awareness as well as your arsenal of mindful actions.

Further, you don't have to go it alone. There are meditation groups, mindfulness classes, and online and in-person retreats. As many of the physicians you read about in these pages did, you can work with a trained mindfulness physician coach. Additionally, you can join the growing group of *Mindful MDs* in the private physician Facebook group* I host by that name. And given that one in two physicians are burned out, you likely know at least a few that you can share your struggles and growth with.

By developing a mindful approach, you can recover a sense of true autonomy even when much going on in healthcare is well beyond your individual control. The system was not designed for your success. Medical training, while well-intentioned, was not designed for your success. And the mind was not designed for your success. You're fighting an uphill battle.

But with consistent effort and mindfulness, you can regain the life and career that you've worked so hard for. You can step out of all the conditioning that plants the seeds and grows the roots of burnout. You can adopt the many mindfulness tools and strategies that will redirect those roots, contributing to the well-being of yourself and those around you. You can truly become the master of your fate, your happiness, and your well-being.

With persistence, patience, and, of course, a big dose of mindfulness, you'll be a happy, balanced, *Mindful MD* before you know it.

---

* - https://www.facebook.com/groups/539466187211003

Epilogue: A New Healthcare

"Be the change you wish to see in the world."
—Mahatma Gandhi

As we move beyond burnout and grow new roots, a great deal becomes possible in our own work and lives, and well beyond. Our enhanced happiness, efficacy, and fulfillment in our posts as doctors has a tremendous ripple effect.

When we experience these changes and move past burnout, our families benefit. They get a more present, happy parent, spouse, and family member. Our friends benefit. Our coworkers benefit. We benefit. And of course, our patients benefit. In this way, we begin to chip away at the dysfunctional, broken healthcare system in the only way that we truly can.

With each moment of presence and mindfulness we bring to our work lives, we help others become more mindful in theirs. With each act of compassion toward one another, we help kindle greater compassion in them. With each upward spiral we invoke, we demonstrate that an upward spiral is possible.

As *Mindful MDs,* we become the force for healing that our healthcare system so desperately needs. Instead of waiting for the system to change, by mindfully becoming that change ourselves, we become the medicine that even a broken system cannot counteract.

If we were to take the same journey we took in the upward spirals chapter and imagine that everyone in healthcare was more mindful, we would begin to see the healing power that mindfulness offers to the entire system.

Imagine a healthcare system where everyone—from the front office staff to the assistant who brings the patient into a room to the technician who draws their blood—is calm and fully present during their time with each patient.

Where all nurses and physicians utilize the compassion practices you learned earlier with their patients, coworkers, and themselves. Imagine how much kinder and empathetic we would each be toward one another.

Where we move beyond the draining force of the beeps, alarms, inboxes, and distractions of the day and truly see the worry, fear, and loneliness of the human beings behind the screens and numbers—and of those of us charged with providing them with care.

Where we are able to smile more comfortably because we're not hypervigilantly preparing to be on the defense or offense.

Where medical training includes an in-depth focus on mindfulness, embracing and utilizing the 6 ways you have now learned and seen in powerful action.

Where the next generation of healers has learned to grow roots that foster their compassion, resilience, growth mindset, and true authentic selves.

You see, at the same time that the forces of corporate healthcare bear down on all of us, I am smiling as I say that this can all be possible. While it is far removed from the healthcare reality we reside in today, each of us can nudge the system in the direction we want it to move.

We become *Mindful MDs* foremost for ourselves: You picked up this book because you are tired of burnout, and you want to live and work in a different way than you currently are.

And I wrote this book so you would have all the tools you need to do so.

In addition to this primary benefit, by assuming true autonomy as a *Mindful MD*, you will be contributing to a new and improved healthcare system. This is not something that will cost millions of dollars to enact. It is not something that has to or can be legislated from above or passed in a partisan political system. But it's a return to the purpose of healthcare—healing and compassion.

Lasting change in healthcare is not going to come from top-down edicts or forces. These bureaucratic rulings only seek to overcomplicate and add friction. You cannot undo bureaucracy with more bureaucracy. And sitting and waiting for a change like this to occur only serves to hand your contentment and well-being over to system that you know is broken.

Instead, today, you can start with yourself. And watch as the benefits ripple further than you could ever imagine.

It is hard to get out of burnout. But let the impact be your motivation. Think about how much your loved ones will benefit. Think of how much your patients will benefit. And think of what the healthcare system will look like as more and more physicians like you take steps to reclaim their careers.

This will only happen when all of us become *Mindful MDs* (and mindful nurses, techs, therapists, aides, administrators, hospital and health system leaders, and others) and bring mindfulness and compassion to all those around us.

You have the power to create this reality.

The problem may very well lie with the system. But the solution, the only solution we have access to, lies with us. It requires stepping out of the reactive blame game of "us" versus "them," and letting go of what we cannot control. It requires being honest about our foibles, whether as a physician, team member, or patient. It requires willingness to see the choices we have, each and every day, in how we show up in our work and lives.

With mindfulness, we see the part each of us plays in shaping the environment around us. We see the choice we have in how we show up each and every day, and with each and every interaction.

We don't always stop and think about the impact that each of our actions has. But each and every one of our actions impacts someone else. Every time we are kind to someone, we build kindness in them. Every time we are harsh or mean, someone has to experience that in their day. Do our actions contribute to the bad day they are already having, perhaps even making them less resilient to the difficulties they face? Or do our actions help them feel good, worthy, and important?

When we are mindful of each our choices, we are better able to show up for our coworkers, and listen to patients with true presence even when we only have 15 minutes to be with that individual. This is the power we each have to make healthcare what we want it to be.

When we mindfully and intentionally consider what it is that we want in healthcare, we can ask ourselves a series of powerful questions:

Am I being part of the solution or part of the problem?

How can I help contribute to the healthcare system I want to see?

What actions can I take today that I will be most proud of?

What can I do to bring out the best in those around me?

What do I want to look back and see?

We can set an intention each and every day to move past frustration, helplessness, and burnout and contribute to the good we want in our healthcare workplaces. By setting an intention, we commit to moving toward the North Star that is important to us. We have a reason greater than ourselves to commit to our own wellbeing and to new patterns that help us thrive. And we have the motivation of the powerful ripple effects that becoming a happy, fulfilled physician who owns their own happiness and career enacts.

To achieve a mindful healthcare system, we each have an important role to play.

Instead of being an impotent pawn in a broken system, we can each be the empowered healers and leaders we are meant to be.

The journey past burnout and toward becoming a participant in righting healthcare begins with a single step.

By setting a firm intention to continue to take these steps, and realigning when you stumble, you can overcome burnout and begin to make this difference. For yourself and for the betterment of all those around you, as a newly minted *Mindful MD*.

NOTES

Introduction

1 Shanafelt, T. D., West, C. P., Sinsky, C., Trockel, M., Tutty, M., Satele, D. V., Carlasare, L. E., & Dyrbye, L. N. (2019). Changes in burnout and satisfaction with work-life integration in physicians and the general US working population between 2011 and 2017. *Mayo Clinic Proceedings, 94*(9), 1681–1694.

2 West, C. P., Dyrbye, L. N., & Shanafelt, T. D. (2018). Physician burnout: Contributors, consequences and solutions. *Journal of Internal Medicine, 283*(6), 516–529.

3 Melnikow, J., Padovani, A., & Miller, M. (2022). Frontline physician burnout during the COVID-19 pandemic: National survey findings. *BMC Health Services Research, 22*(1), 1–8.

4 Sharifi, M., Asadi-Pooya, A. A., & Mousavi-Roknabadi, R. S. (2021). Burnout among healthcare providers of COVID-19; a systematic review of epidemiology and recommendations. *Archives of Academic Emergency Medicine, 9*(1), e7.

5 Mata, D. A., Ramos, M. A., Bansal, N., Khan, R., Guille, C., Di Angelantonio, E., & Sen, S. (2015). Prevalence of depression and depressive symptoms among resident physicians: A systematic review and meta-analysis. *JAMA, 314*(22), 2373–2383.

6 Goldman, M. L., Shah, R. N., & Bernstein, C. A. (2015). Depression and suicide among physician trainees: Recommendations for a national response. *JAMA Psychiatry, 72*(5), 411–412.

7 Dyrbye, L. N., Thomas, M. R., & Shanafelt, T. D. (2006).

Systematic review of depression, anxiety, and other indicators of psychological distress among US and Canadian medical students. *Academic Medicine: Journal of the Association of American Medical Colleges, 81*(4), 354–373.

8 Eckleberry-Hunt, J., & Lick, D. (2015). Physician depression and suicide: A shared responsibility. *Teaching and Learning in Medicine, 27*(3), 341–345.

9 Middleton, J. L. (2021). Preventing physician suicide. *American Family Physician, 103*(7), 396.

10 Kuhn, C. M., & Flanagan, E. M. (2017). Self-care as a professional imperative: Physician burnout, depression, and suicide. *Canadian Journal of Anesthesia/Journal canadien d'anesthésie, 64*(2), 158–168.

11 Albuquerque, J., & Tulk, S. (2019). Physician suicide. *CMAJ: Canadian Medical Association Journal/Journal de l'association medicale canadienne, 191*(18), E505.

12 Gulati, G., & Kelly, B. D. (2020). Physician suicide and the COVID-19 pandemic. *Occupational Medicine, 70*(7), 514.

13 Al-Ghunaim, T. A., Johnson, J., Biyani, C. S., Alshahrani, K. M., Dunning, A., & O'Connor, D. B. (2021). Surgeon burnout, impact on patient safety and professionalism: A systematic review and meta-analysis. *The American Journal of Surgery, 224*(1), 228–238.

14 Owoc, J., Mańczak, M., Jabłońska, M., Tombarkiewicz, M., & Olszewski, R. (2022). Association between physician burnout and self-reported errors: Meta-analysis. *Journal of Patient Safety, 18*(1), e180–e188.

15 Tawfik, D. S., Profit, J., Morgenthaler, T. I., Satele, D. V., Sinsky, C. A., Dyrbye, L. N., Tutty, M. A., West, C. P., & Shanafelt, T. D. (2018). Physician burnout, well-being, and work unit safety grades in relationship to reported medical errors. *Mayo Clinic Proceedings, 93*(11), 1571–1580.

16 Trockel, M. T., Menon, N. K., Rowe, S. G., Stewart, M. T., Smith, R., Lu, M., Kim, P. K., Quinn, M. A., Lawrence,

E., Marcharlik, D., Farley, H., Normand, P., Felder, M., Dudley, J. C., & Shanafelt, T. D. (2020). Assessment of physician sleep and wellness, burnout, and clinically significant medical errors. *JAMA Network Open*, *3*(12), e2028111.

17 Wilkinson, H., Whittington, R., Perry, L., & Eames, C. (2017). Examining the relationship between burnout and empathy in healthcare professionals: A systematic review. *Burnout Research*, *6*, 18–29.

18 Picard, J., Catu-Pinault, A., Boujut, E., Botella, M., Jaury, P., & Zenasni, F. (2016). Burnout, empathy and their relationships: A qualitative study with residents in General Medicine. *Psychology, Health & Medicine*, *21*(3), 354–361.

19 Salyers, M. P., Bonfils, K. A., Luther, L., Firmin, R. L., White, D. A., Adams, E. L., & Rollins, A. L. (2017). The relationship between professional burnout and quality and safety in healthcare: A meta-analysis. *Journal of General Internal Medicine*, *32*(4), 475–482.

20 Hancock, J., Witter, T., Comber, S., Daley, P., Thompson, K., Candow, S., Follett, G., Somers, W., Collins, C., White, J., & Kits, O. (2020). Understanding burnout and moral distress to build resilience: A qualitative study of an interprofessional intensive care unit team. *Canadian Journal of Anesthesia/Journal canadien d'anesthésie*, *67*(11), 1541–1548.

The Roots of Burnout

1 Ofri, D. (2013). *What doctors feel: How emotions affect the practice of medicine*. Beacon Press.

2 Gladwell, M. (2014). *David and Goliath*. Penguin Books.

3 Brazeau, C. M., Shanafelt, T., Durning, S. J., Massie, F. S., Eacker, A., Moutier, C., Satele, D. V., Sloan, J. A., & Dyrbye, L. N. (2014). Distress among matriculating medical students relative to the general population.

Academic Medicine, 89(11), 1520–1525.

4 Dyrbye, L. N., Harper, W., Durning, S. J., Moutier, C., Thomas, M. R., Massie, F. S., Jr, Eacker, A., Power, D. V., Szydlo, D. W., Sloan, J. A., & Shanafelt, T. D. (2011). Patterns of distress in US medical students. *Medical teacher, 33*(10), 834–839.

5 Dyrbye, L., & Shanafelt, T. (2016) A narrative review on burnout experienced by medical students and residents. *Medical Education, 50*(1), 132–149.

6 Hope, V., & Henderson, M. (2014). Medical student depression, anxiety and distress outside North America: A systematic review. *Medical education, 48*(10), 963–979.

7 Blanchard, C., Kravets, V., Schenker, M., & Moore, T., Jr. (2021). Emotional intelligence, burnout, and professional fulfillment in clinical year medical students. *Medical Teacher, 43*(9), 1063–1069.

8 Rodrigues, H., Cobucci, R., Oliveira, A., Cabral, J. V., Medeiros, L., Gurgel, K., Souza, T., & Gonçalves, A. K. (2018). Burnout syndrome among medical residents: A systematic review and meta-analysis. *PloS one, 13*(11), e0206840.

9 Ibid.

10 Hojat, M., Vergare, M. J., Maxwell, K., Brainard, G., Herrine, S. K., Isenberg, G. A., Veloski, J., & Gonnella, J. S. (2009). The devil is in the third year: A longitudinal study of erosion of empathy in medical school. *Academic Medicine, 84*(9), 1182–1191.

11 Wang, C. X. Y., Pavlova, A., Boggiss, A. L., O'Callaghan, A., & Consedine, N. S. (2022). Predictors of medical students' compassion and related constructs: A systematic review. *Teaching and Learning in Medicine,* 1–12.

12 Mahoney, S., Sladek, R. M., & Neild, T. (2016). A longitudinal study of empathy in pre-clinical and clinical medical students and clinical supervisors. *BMC medical education, 16*(1), 1–8.

13 Verghese, A. (2009, May 27) Empathy: Good for doctors and bad for judges? *The Atlantic.* https://www.theatlantic. com/technology/archive/2009/05/empathy-good-for-doctors-and-bad-for-judges/18375/

14 Batt-Rawden, S. A., Chisolm, M. S., Anton, B., & Flickinger, T. E. (2013). Teaching empathy to medical students: An updated, systematic review. *Academic Medicine, 88*(8), 1171–1177.

15 Newton, B. W., Barber, L., Clardy, J., Cleveland, E., & O'Sullivan, P. (2008). Is there hardening of the heart during medical school? *Academic Medicine, 83*(3), 244–249.

16 Pearl, Robert. (2021). *Uncaring: How the culture of medicine kills doctors & patients.* PublicAffairs.

17 Peadon, R., Hurley, J., & Hutchinson, M. (2020). Hierarchy and medical error: Speaking up when witnessing an error. *Safety Science, 125*, 104648.

18 Louie, A. K., Roberts, L. W., & Coverdale, J. (2007). The enculturation of medical students and residents. *Academic Psychiatry, 31*(4), 253–257.

19 Lehmann, L. S., Sulmasy, L. S., Desai, S., & ACP Ethics, Professionalism and Human Rights Committee. (2018). Hidden curricula, ethics, and professionalism: Optimizing clinical learning environments in becoming and being a physician: A position paper of the American College of Physicians. *Annals of Internal Medicine, 168*(7), 506–508.

20 Martimianakis, M. A. T., Michalec, B., Lam, J., Cartmill, C., Taylor, J. S., & Hafferty, F. W. (2015). Humanism, the hidden curriculum, and educational reform: A scoping review and thematic analysis. *Academic Medicine, 90*(11), S5–S13.

21 Dhaliwal, G., & Hauer, K. E. (2021). Excellence in medical training: Developing talent—not sorting it. *Perspectives on Medical Education, 10*(6), 356–361.

22 Joseph, R. (2018). A look in the mirror: The role of medical

training in physician burnout. *NEJM Catalyst, 4*(1).

23 Richardson, D., Kinnear, B., Hauer, K. E., Turner, T. L., Warm, E. J., Hall, A. K., Ross, S., Thoma, B., Van Melle, E., & ICBME Collaborators. (2021). Growth mindset in competency-based medical education. *Medical Teacher, 43*(7), 751–757.

24 Bynum IV, W. E., Artino, A. R., Jr, Uijtdehaage, S., Webb, A. M. B., & Varpio, L. (2019). Sentinel emotional events: The nature, triggers, and effects of shame experiences in medical residents. *Academic Medicine, 94*(1), 85–93.

25 Lind, K. T., Osborne, C. M., Badesch, B., Blood, A., & Lowenstein, S. R. (2020). Ending student mistreatment: early successes and continuing challenges. *Medical Education Online, 25*(1), 1690846.

26 Miles, S. (2020). Addressing shame: What role does shame play in the formation of a modern medical professional identity? *BJPsych Bulletin, 44*(1), 1–5.

27 Enns, M. W., Cox, B. J., Sareen, J., & Freeman, P. (2001). Adaptive and maladaptive perfectionism in medical students: A longitudinal investigation. *Medical Education, 35*(11), 1034–1042.

28 Eley, D. S., Bansal, V., & Leung, J. (2020). Perfectionism as a mediator of psychological distress: Implications for addressing underlying vulnerabilities to the mental health of medical students. *Medical Teacher, 42*(11), 1301–1307.

29 Martin, S. R., Fortier, M. A., Heyming, T. W., Ahn, K., Nichols, W., Golden, C., Saadat, H., & Kain, Z. N. (2022). Perfectionism as a predictor of physician burnout. *BMC Health Services Research, 22*(1), 1425.

30 Peters, M., & King, J. (2012). Perfectionism in doctors. *BMJ, 344*, e1674.

31 Thomson, I. (2017). Do "good" medical students really make good doctors? *Academic Medicine, 92*(6), 735.

32 Yanes, A. F. (2017). The culture of perfection: A barrier to medical student wellness and development. *Academic*

Medicine, 92(7), 900–901.

33 Lee, T. H. (2010, April). Turning doctors into leaders. *Harvard Business Review.* https://hbr.org/2010/04/turning-doctors-into-leaders

34 Weinstein, M. S. (2018). Out of the straitjacket. *The New England Journal of Medicine, 378*(9), 793–795.

35 Joseph, R. (2018). A look in the mirror: The role of medical training in physician burnout. *NEJM Catalyst, 4*(1).

36 Kishore, S., Ripp, J., Shanafelt, T., Melnyk, B., Rogers, D., Brigham, T., Busis, N., Charney, D., Cipriano, P., Minor, L., Rothman, P., Spisso, J., Kirch, D. G., Nasca, T. & Dzau, V. (2018). Making the case for the chief wellness officer in America's health systems: A call to action. *Health Affairs Blog, 10,* 1377. https://www.healthaffairs.org/do/10.1377/forefront.20181025.308059/

37 Caceres, J. W., & Lizotte-Waniewski, M. (2021). Addressing medical student wellness over the long term: How should we be evaluating wellness programs? *Medical Science Educator, 31*(2), 877–878.

38 Sullivan, A. G., Hoffman, A., & Slavin, S. (2020). Becoming AWARE: ACGME's new suite of well-being resources. *Journal of Graduate Medical Education, 12*(1), 122–124.

39 Bodenheimer, T., & Sinsky, C. (2014). From triple to quadruple aim: Care of the patient requires care of the provider. *Annals of Family Medicine, 12*(6), 573–576.

40 Eskander, J., Rajaguru, P. P., & Greenberg, P. B. (2021). Evaluating wellness interventions for resident physicians: A systematic review. *Journal of Graduate Medical Education, 13*(1), 58–69.

41 See below for a short list of resources from professional societies who have taken steps to address the topic of healthcare worker wellness:

- American Medical Association Steps Forward: https://edhub.ama-assn.org/steps-forward

- American Academy of Family Physicians: https://

www.aafp.org/family-physician/practice-and-career/
managing-your-career/physician-well-being.html

- Association of American Medical Colleges:
  https://www.aamc.org/professional-development/af-
  finity-groups/gfa/well-being-and-resilience-resources
- American College of Graduate Medical Education:
  https://dl.acgme.org/pages/well-being
- British Medical Association: https://www.bma.org.uk/
  advice-and-support/your-wellbeing
- Canadian Medical Association: https://www.cma.ca/
  physician-wellness-hub
- American College of Physicians: https://www.acp-
  online.org/practice-resources/physician-well-be-
  ing-and-professional-fulfillment
- American College of Surgeons:
  https://www.facs.org/for-medical-professionals/pro-
  fessional-growth-and-wellness/surgeon-wellbeing/
  resources/
- American College of Cardiology: https://www.acc.org/
  clinicianwellbeing
- American College of Emergency Physicians: https://
  www.acep.org/emwellness/

42 Miles, S. (2020). Addressing shame: What role does shame play in the formation of a modern medical professional identity? *BJPsych Bulletin, 44*(1), 1–5.

43 Bynum IV, W. E., Artino Jr, A. R., Uijtdehaage, S., Webb, A. M., & Varpio, L. (2019). Sentinel emotional events: The nature, triggers, and effects of shame experiences in medical residents. *Academic Medicine, 94*(1), 85–93.

44 Robertson, J. J., & Long, B. (2019). Medicine's shame

problem. *The Journal of Emergency Medicine, 57*(3), 329–338.

45 Colenbrander, L., Causer, L., & Haire, B. (2020). 'If you can't make it, you're not tough enough to do medicine': A qualitative study of Sydney-based medical students' experiences of bullying and harassment in clinical settings. *BMC Medical Education, 20*, 1–12.

46 Whelan, B., Hjörleifsson, S., & Schei, E. (2021). Shame in medical clerkship: "You just feel like dirt under someone's shoe." *Perspectives on Medical Education, 10*(5), 265–271.

Recognize That You Are Not Your Thoughts

1 Pavlova, A., Wang, C. X. Y., Boggiss, A. L., O'Callaghan, A., & Consedine, N. S. (2022). Predictors of physician compassion, empathy, and related constructs: A systematic review. *Journal of General Internal Medicine, 37*(4), 900–911.

2 Emanuel, E. J., & Gudbranson, E. (2018). Does medicine overemphasize IQ? *JAMA, 319*(7), 651–652.

3 Tseng, J., & Poppenk, J. (2020). Brain meta-state transitions demarcate thoughts across task contexts exposing the mental noise of trait neuroticism. *Nature communications, 11*(1), 1–12.

4 Klein, R. J., & Robinson, M. D. (2019). Neuroticism as mental noise: Evidence from a continuous tracking task. *Journal of Personality, 87*(6), 1221–1233.

5 Lamott, A. (1995). *Bird by bird: Some instructions on writing and life.* Knopf Doubleday Publishing Group.

6 Williams, M., & Penman, D. (2011). *Mindfulness: An eight-week plan for finding peace in a frantic world.* Rodale Press.

Step Out of Mental Stories

1 Jung, C. G. (1953). *The collected works of C. G. Jung.* Princeton University Press.

2 Brewer, J. (2021). *Unwinding anxiety: New science shows how to break the cycles of worry and fear to heal your mind.* Avery Press.

Reduce Reactivity

1 Sataloff, R. T. (2020). Emotional intelligence and physician wellness. *Ear, Nose & Throat Journal, 99*(3), 157–158.
2 Lin, D. T., Liebert, C. A., Tran, J., Lau, J. N., & Salles, A. (2016). Emotional intelligence as a predictor of resident well-being. *Journal of the American College of Surgeons, 223*(2), 352–358.
3 Weng, H. C. (2008). Does the physician's emotional intelligence matter? Impacts of the physician's emotional intelligence on the trust, patient-physician relationship, and satisfaction. *Health Care Management Review, 33*(4), 280–288.
4 Suhaimi, N. S., Mountstephens, J., & Teo, J. (2020). EEG-based emotion recognition: A state-of-the-art review of current trends and opportunities. *Computational Intelligence and Neuroscience. 2020,* 1–19.
5 Feldman Barrett, L. (2017). *How emotions are made: The secret life of the brain.* Harper Collins Publishers.
6 McRae, K., & Gross, J. J. (2020). Emotion regulation. *Emotion, 20*(1), 1–9.
7 Marturano, J. (2014). *Finding the space to lead: A practical guide to mindful leadership.* Bloomsbury Publishing USA.
8 Drew, T., Võ, M. L.-H., & Wolfe, J. M. (2013). The invisible gorilla strikes again: Sustained inattentional blindness in expert observers. *Psychological Science, 24*(9), 1848–1853.
9 Hoge, E. A., Bui, E., Marques, L., Metcalf, C. A., Morris, L. K., Robinaugh, D. J., Worthington, J. J., Pollack, M. H., & Simon, N. M. (2013). Randomized controlled trial of mindfulness meditation for generalized anxiety disorder: Effects on anxiety and stress reactivity. *The Journal of Clinical Psychiatry, 74*(8), 786–792.
10 Saeed, S. A., Cunningham, K., & Bloch, R. M. (2019).

Depression and anxiety disorders: Benefits of exercise, yoga, and meditation. *American Family Physician, 99*(10), 620–627.

11 Koncz, A., Demetrovics, Z., & Takacs, Z. K. (2021). Meditation interventions efficiently reduce cortisol levels of at-risk samples: A meta-analysis. *Health Psychology Review, 15*(1), 56–84.

12 Chin, B., Lindsay, E. K., Greco, C. M., Brown, K. W., Smyth, J. M., Wright, A. G. C., & Creswell, J. D. (2019). Psychological mechanisms driving stress resilience in mindfulness training: A randomized controlled trial. *Health Psychology, 38*(8), 759–768.

13 Zhou, X., Guo, J., Lu, G., Chen, C., Xie, Z., Liu, J., & Zhang, C. (2020). Effects of mindfulness-based stress reduction on anxiety symptoms in young people: A systematic review and meta-analysis. *Psychiatry Research, 289*, 113002.

14 Komariah, M., Ibrahim, K., Pahria, T., Rahayuwati, L., & Somantri, I. (2023). Effect of mindfulness breathing meditation on depression, anxiety, and stress: A randomized controlled trial among university students. *Healthcare, 11*(1), 26.

15 Jain, F. A., Walsh, R. N., Eisendrath, S. J., Christe5 nsen, S., & Rael Cahn, B. (2015). Critical analysis of the efficacy of meditation therapies for acute and subacute phase treatment of depressive disorders: A systematic review. *Psychosomatics, 56*(2), 140–152.

16 Norris, C. J., Creem, D., Hendler, R., & Kober, H. (2018). Brief mindfulness meditation improves attention in novices: Evidence from ERPs and moderation by neuroticism. *Frontiers in Human Neuroscience, 12*, 315.

17 Basso, J. C., McHale, A., Ende, V., Oberlin, D. J., & Suzuki, W. A. (2019). Brief, daily meditation enhances attention, memory, mood, and emotional regulation in non-experienced meditators. *Behavioural Brain Research, 356*, 208–220.

18 Wolkin, J. R. (2015). Cultivating multiple aspects of

attention through mindfulness meditation accounts for psychological well-being through decreased rumination. *Psychology Research and Behavior Management, 8*, 171–180.

19 Lavadera, P., Millon, E. M., & Shors, T. J. (2020). MAP train my brain: Meditation combined with aerobic exercise reduces stress and rumination while enhancing quality of life in medical students. *The Journal of Alternative and Complementary Medicine, 26*(5), 418–423.

20 Lodha, S., & Gupta, R. (2022). Mindfulness, attentional networks, and executive functioning: A review of interventions and long-term meditation practice. *Journal of Cognitive Enhancement, 6*(4), 531–548.

21 Schneider, J. K., Reangsing, C., & Willis, D. G. (2022). Effects of transcendental meditation on blood pressure: A meta-analysis. *Journal of Cardiovascular Nursing, 37*(3), E11–E21.

22 Ponte Márquez, P. H., Feliu-Soler, A., Solé-Villa, M. J., Matas-Pericas, L., Filella-Agullo, D., Ruiz-Herrerias, M., Soler-Ribaudi, J., Roca-Cusachs Coll, A., & Arroyo-Díaz, J. A. (2019). Benefits of mindfulness meditation in reducing blood pressure and stress in patients with arterial hypertension. *Journal of Human Hypertension, 33*(3), 237–247.

23 Hilton, L., Hempel, S., Ewing, B. A., Apaydin, E., Xenakis, L., Newberry, S., Colaiaco, B., Maher, A. R., Shanman, R. M., Sorbero, M. E., & Maglione, M. A. (2017). Mindfulness meditation for chronic pain: Systematic review and meta-analysis. *Annals of Behavioral Medicine, 51*(2), 199–213.

24 Pei, J. H., Ma, T., Nan, R. L., Chen, H. X., Zhang, Y. B., Gou, L., & Dou, X. M. (2021). Mindfulness-based cognitive therapy for treating chronic pain: A systematic review and meta-analysis. *Psychology, Health & Medicine, 26*(3), 333–346.

25 Khalsa, D. S. (2015). Stress, meditation, and Alzheimer's disease prevention: Where the evidence stands. *Journal*

of Alzheimer's Disease, 48(1), 1–12.

26 Krasner, M. S., Epstein, R. M., Beckman, H., Suchman, A. L., Chapman, B., Mooney, C. J., & Quill, T. E. (2009). Association of an educational program in mindful communication with burnout, empathy, and attitudes among primary care physicians. *JAMA, 302*(12), 1284–1293.

27 Spinelli, C., Wisener, M., & Khoury, B. (2019). Mindfulness training for healthcare professionals and trainees: A meta-analysis of randomized controlled trials. *Journal of Psychosomatic Research, 120*, 29–38.

28 Roy, A., Druker, S., Hoge, E. A., & Brewer, J. A. (2020). Physician anxiety and burnout: Symptom correlates and a prospective pilot study of app-delivered mindfulness training. *JMIR mHealth and uHealth, 8*(4), e15608.

29 Scheepers, R. A., Emke, H., Epstein, R. M., & Lombarts, K. M. (2020). The impact of mindfulness-based interventions on doctors' well-being and performance: A systematic review. *Medical education, 54*(2), 138–149.

30 Ireland, M. J., Clough, B., Gill, K., Langan, F., O'Connor, A., & Spencer, L. (2017). A randomized controlled trial of mindfulness to reduce stress and burnout among intern medical practitioners. *Medical Teacher, 39*(4), 409–414.

31 Aryankhesal, A., Mohammadibakhsh, R., Hamidi, Y., Alidoost, S., Behzadifar, M., Sohrabi, R., & Farhadi, Z. (2019). Interventions on reducing burnout in physicians and nurses: A systematic review. *Medical journal of the Islamic Republic of Iran, 33*, 77.

32 Schroeder, D. A., Stephens, E., Colgan, D., Hunsinger, M., Rubin, D., & Christopher, M. S. (2016). A brief mindfulness-based intervention for primary care physicians: A pilot randomized controlled trial. *American Journal of Lifestyle Medicine, 12*(1), 83–91.

33 Rosdahl, J. A., & Kingsolver, K. (2014). Mindfulness training to increase resilience and decrease stress and burnout in ophthalmology residents: A pilot study. *Investigative*

Ophthalmology & Visual Science, 55(13), 5579–5579.

34 Gracia Gozalo, R. M., Ferrer Tarrés, J. M., Ayora Ayora, A., Alonso Herrero, M., Amutio Kareaga, A., & Ferrer Roca, R. (2019). Application of a mindfulness program among healthcare professionals in an intensive care unit: Effect on burnout, empathy and self-compassion. *Medicina Intensiva (English Edition), 43*(4), 207–216.

35 Fendel, J. C., Bürkle, J. J., & Göritz, A. S. (2021). Mindfulness-based interventions to reduce burnout and stress in physicians: A systematic review and meta-analysis. *Academic Medicine, 96*(5), 751–764.

36 Verweij, H., van Ravesteijn, H., Lagro-Janssen. A. L. M., & Speckens, A. E. M. (2018) Mindfulness-based stress reduction for residents: A randomized controlled trial. Journal of General Internal Medicine, *33*(4), 429–436.

37 Lebares, C. C., Guvva, E. V., Olaru, M., Sugrue, L. P., Staffaroni, A. M., Delucchi, K. L., Kramer, J. H., Ascher, N. L., & Harris, H. W. (2019). Efficacy of mindfulness-based cognitive training in surgery: Additional analysis of the mindful surgeon pilot randomized clinical trial. JAMA Network Open, *2*(5), e194108.

38 Nguyen, M. C., Gabbe, S. G., Kemper, K. J., Mahan, J. D., Cheavens, J. S., & Moffatt-Bruce, S. D. (2020). Training on mind-body skills: Feasibility and effects on physician mindfulness, compassion, and associated effects on stress, burnout, and clinical outcomes. *The Journal of Positive Psychology, 15*(2), 194–207.

39 Fortney, L., Luchterhand, C., Zakletskaia, L., Zgierska, A., & Rakel, D. (2013). Abbreviated mindfulness intervention for job satisfaction, quality of life, and compassion in primary care clinicians: A pilot study. *The Annals of Family Medicine, 11*(5), 412–420.

40 Fendel, J. C., Bürkle, J. J., & Göritz, A. S. (2021). Mindfulness-based interventions to reduce burnout and stress in physicians: A systematic review and meta-analysis. *Academic Medicine, 96*(5), 751–764.

41 Lebares, C. C., Guvva, E. V., Olaru, M., Sugrue, L. P., Staffaroni, A. M., Delucchi, K. L., Kramer, J. H., Ascher, N. L., & Harris, H. W. (2019). Efficacy of mindfulness-based cognitive training in surgery: Additional analysis of the mindful surgeon pilot randomized clinical trial. JAMA Network Open, 2(5), e194108.

42 Verweij, H., van Ravesteijn, H., Lagro-Janssen. A. L. M., & Speckens, A. E. M. (2018) Mindfulness-based stress reduction for residents: A randomized controlled trial. Journal of General Internal Medicine, 33(4), 429–436.

43 Amutio, A., Martínez-Taboada, C., Delgado, L. C., Hermosilla, D., Mozaz, M. J. (2015). Acceptability and effectiveness of a long-term educational intervention to reduce physicians' stress-related conditions. *Journal of Continuing Education in the Health Professions, 35*(4), 255–260.

44 Franco Justo, C. (2010). Reducción de los niveles de estrés y ansiedad en médicos de Atención Primaria mediante la aplicación de un programa de entrenamiento en conciencia plena (mindfulness) [Reducing stress levels and anxiety in primary-care physicians through training and practice of a mindfulness meditation technique]. *Atencion Primaria, 42*(11), 564–570.

45 Schroeder, D. A., Stephens, E., Colgan, D., Hunsinger, M., Rubin, D., & Christopher, M. S. (2016). A brief mindfulness-based intervention for primary care physicians: A pilot randomized controlled trial. *American Journal of Lifestyle Medicine, 12*(1), 83–91.

46 Ireland, M. J., Clough, B., Gill, K., Langan, F., O'Connor, A., & Spencer, L. (2017). A randomized controlled trial of mindfulness to reduce stress and burnout among intern medical practitioners. *Medical Teacher, 39*(4), 409–414.

Lean Into Compassion, Connection, and Purpose

1 Fox, J., & Meisenberg, B. (2022). The 3-fold harms of compassion fatigue during COVID-19 surges. *The*

American Journal of Medicine, 135(8), e234–e235.

2 Forrest, L., Abdurrahman, M., & Ritsma, A. (2020). Recognizing compassion fatigue, vicarious trauma, and burnout. In A. Hategan, K. Saperson, S. Harms, & H. Waters (Eds.), *Humanism and resilience in residency training: A guide to physician wellness* (pp. 297–330). Springer.

3 Nichols, S. R., Svetlova, M., & Brownell, C. A. (2015). Toddlers' responses to infants' negative emotions. *Infancy, 20*(1), 70–97.

4 Roth-Hanania, R., Davidov, M., & Zahn-Waxler, C. (2011). Empathy development from 8 to 16 months: Early signs of concern for others. *Infant Behavior and Development, 34*(3), 447–458.

5 Spinrad, T. L., & Eisenberg, N. (2017). Compassion in children. In E. M. Seppälä, Simon-Thomas, E., Brown, S. L., Worline, M. C., Cameron, C. D., & Doty, J. R. (Eds.), *The Oxford handbook of compassion science* (pp. 53–64). Oxford University Press.

6 Warneken, F., & Tomasello, M. (2006). Altruistic helping in human infants and young chimpanzees. *Science, 311*(5765), 1301–1303.

7 Saturn, S. R. (2017). Two factors that fuel compassion: The oxytocin system and the social experience of moral elevation. In E. M. Seppälä, Simon-Thomas, E., Brown, S. L., Worline, M. C., Cameron, C. D., & Doty, J. R. (Eds.), *Oxford handbook of compassion science* (pp. 121–132). Oxford University Press.

8 Kucerova, B., Levit-Binnun, N., Gordon, I., & Golland, Y. (2023). From oxytocin to compassion: The saliency of distress. *Biology, 12*(2), 183.

9 Newton, B. W., Barber, L., Clardy, J., Cleveland, E., & O'Sullivan, P. (2008). Is there hardening of the heart during medical school? *Academic Medicine, 83*(3), 244–249.

10 Hegazi, I., & Wilson, I. (2013). Maintaining empathy in

medical school: It is possible. *Medical Teacher, 35*(12), 1002–1008.

11 Hojat, M., Vergare, M. J., Maxwell, K., Brainard, G., Herrine, S. K., Isenberg, G. A., Veloski, J., & Gonnella, J. S. (2009). The devil is in the third year: A longitudinal study of erosion of empathy in medical school. *Academic Medicine, 84*(9), 1182–1191.

12 Igde, F. A., & Sahin, M. K. (2017). Changes in empathy during medical education: An example from Turkey. *Pakistan Journal of Medical Sciences, 33*(5), 1177–1181.

13 Coulehan, J. (2005). Today's professionalism: Engaging the mind but not the heart. *Academic Medicine, 80*(10), 892–898.

14 Newton, B. W., Barber, L., Clardy, J., Cleveland, E., & O'Sullivan, P. (2008). Is there hardening of the heart during medical school? *Academic Medicine, 83*(3), 244–249.

15 Wang, C. X. Y., Pavlova, A., Boggiss, A. L., O'Callaghan, A., & Consedine, N. S. (2022). Predictors of medical students' compassion and related constructs: A systematic review. *Teaching and learning in medicine,* 1–12.

16 Hojat, M., Vergare, M. J., Maxwell, K., Brainard, G., Herrine, S. K., Isenberg, G. A., Veloski, J., & Gonnella, J. S. (2009). The devil is in the third year: A longitudinal study of erosion of empathy in medical school. *Academic Medicine, 84*(9), 1182–1191.

17 Menezes, P., Guraya, S. Y., & Guraya, S. S. (2021). A systematic review of educational interventions and their impact on empathy and compassion of undergraduate medical students. *Frontiers in Medicine, 8,* 758377.

18 Hegazi, I., & Wilson, I. (2013). Maintaining empathy in medical school: It is possible. *Medical Teacher, 35*(12), 1002–1008.

19 Verghese, A. (2009, May 27) Empathy: Good for doctors and bad for judges? *The Atlantic.* https://www.theatlantic.

com/technology/archive/2009/05/empathy-good-for-doctors-and-bad-for-judges/18375/

20 Nevalainen, M., Kuikka, L., Sjöberg, L., Eriksson, J., & Pitkälä, K. (2012). Tolerance of uncertainty and fears of making mistakes among fifth-year medical students. *Family Medicine, 44*(4), 240–246.

21 Shahaf-Oren, B., Madan, I., & Henderson, C. (2021). "A lot of medical students, their biggest fear is failing at being seen to be a functional human": Disclosure and help-seeking decisions by medical students with health problems. *BMC Medical Education, 21*(1), 1–10.

22 Burney, C. P., Goldwag, J. L., Sorensen, M. J., & Crockett, A. O. (2021). Hopes, fears, and rumors: Medical students and the general surgery clerkship. *The American Journal of Surgery, 222*(4), 687–691.

23 Kim, J. J., Cunnington, R., & Kirby, J. N. (2020). The neurophysiological basis of compassion: An fMRI meta-analysis of compassion and its related neural processes. *Neuroscience & biobehavioral reviews, 108*, 112–123.

24 Smith, C., & Davidson, H. (2014). *The paradox of generosity: Giving we receive, grasping we lose.* Oxford University Press, USA.

25 Preston, S. D. (2017). The rewarding nature of social contact. *Science, 357*(6358), 1353–1354.

26 Mangels, D. (2009). The science of happiness. *Berkeley Scientific Journal, 12*(2).

27 Ashar, Y. K., Andrews-Hanna, J. R., Halifax, J., Dimidjian, S., & Wager, T. D. (2021). Effects of compassion training on brain responses to suffering others. *Social cognitive and affective neuroscience, 16*(10), 1036–1047.

28 Pavlova, A., Wang, C. X. Y., Boggiss, A. L., O'Callaghan, A., & Consedine, N. S. (2022). Predictors of physician compassion, empathy, and related constructs: A systematic review. Journal of General Internal Medicine, 37(4), 900–911.

29 Babenko, O., Mosewich, A. D., Lee, A., & Koppula, S.

(2019). Association of physicians' self-compassion with work engagement, exhaustion, and professional life satisfaction. *Medical Sciences, 7*(2), 29.

30 Kemper, K. J., McClafferty, H., Wilson, P. M., Serwint, J. R., Batra, M., Mahan, J. D., Schubert, C. J., Staples, B. B., Schwartz, A., & Pediatric Resident Burnout-Resilience Study Consortium (2019). Do mindfulness and self-compassion predict burnout in pediatric residents? *Academic Medicine, 94*(6), 876–884.

31 Richardson, D. A., Jaber, S., Chan, S., Jesse, M. T., Kaur, H., & Sangha, R. (2016). Self-compassion and empathy: Impact on burnout and secondary traumatic stress in medical training. *Open Journal of Epidemiology, 6*(3), 161–166.

32 Coleman, M. (2016). *Make peace with your mind: How mindfulness and compassion can free you from your inner critic.* New World Library.

33 Solomon, M. F., & Siegel, D. J. (Eds.). (2017). *How people change: Relationships and neuroplasticity in psychotherapy.* Norton Series on Interpersonal Neurobiology.

34 Parrish, M. H., Inagaki, T. K., Muscatell, K. A., Haltom, K. E. B., Leary, M. R., & Eisenberger, N. I. (2018). Self-compassion and responses to negative social feedback: The role of fronto-amygdala circuit connectivity. *Self and Identity, 17*(6), 723–738.

35 Doerig, N., Schlumpf, Y., Spinelli, S., Späti, J., Brakowski, J., Quednow, B. B., Seifritz, E., & Grosse Holtforth, M. (2014). Neural representation and clinically relevant moderators of individualised self-criticism in healthy subjects. *Social Cognitive and Affective Neuroscience, 9*(9), 1333–1340.

36 Germer, C., & Neff, K. (2019). Mindful self-compassion (MSC). In I. Ivtzan (Ed.), *Handbook of mindfulness-based programmes: Mindfulness interventions from education to health and therapy* (pp. 357–367). Routledge.

37 Salzberg, S. (2017). *Real love: The art of mindful connection.* Flatiron Books.

38 Keller, S., & Huppert, F. A. (2021). The virtue of self-compassion. *Ethical Theory and Moral Practice, 24*(2), 443–458.

39 López, A., Sanderman, R., Ranchor, A. V., & Schroevers, M. J. (2018). Compassion for others and self-compassion: Levels, correlates, and relationship with psychological well-being. *Mindfulness, 9*(1), 325–331.

40 Umphrey, L. R., & Sherblom, J. C. (2014). The relationship of hope to self-compassion, relational social skill, communication apprehension, and life satisfaction. *International Journal of Wellbeing, 4*(2), 1–18.

41 Babenko, O., Mosewich, A. D., Lee, A., & Koppula, S. (2019). Association of physicians' self-compassion with work engagement, exhaustion, and professional life satisfaction. *Medical Sciences, 7*(2), 29.

42 Kemper, K. J., McClafferty, H., Wilson, P. M., Serwint, J. R., Batra, M., Mahan, J. D., Schubert, C. J., Staples, B. B., Schwartz, A., & Pediatric Resident Burnout-Resilience Study Consortium (2019). Do mindfulness and self-compassion predict burnout in pediatric residents? Academic Medicine, *94*(6), 876–884.

43 Richardson, D. A., Jaber, S., Chan, S., Jesse, M. T., Kaur, H., & Sangha, R. (2016). Self-compassion and empathy: Impact on burnout and secondary traumatic stress in medical training. *Open Journal of Epidemiology, 6*(3), 161–166.

Work With What Is

1 Larsson, E. W., & Stern, T. A. (2013). Helplessness in the helpers: Etiology and management. *The Primary Care Companion for CNS Disorders, 15*(6), 27316.

2 Abramson, L. Y., Seligman, M. E., & Teasdale, J. D. (1978). Learned helplessness in humans: Critique and reformulation. *Journal of Abnormal Psychology, 87*(1), 49–74.

3 Larsson, E. W., & Stern, T. A. (2013). Helplessness in the

helpers: Etiology and management. *The Primary Care Companion for CNS Disorders*, *15*(6), 27316.

4 Southwick, S. M., & Southwick, F. S. (2020). The loss of social connectedness as a major contributor to physician burnout: Applying organizational and teamwork principles for prevention and recovery. *JAMA Psychiatry*, *77*(5), 449–450.

5 Bond, C. (2007). The training of the "helpless" physician. *Medscape General Medicine*, *9*(3), 47.

6 Nhah Hanh, T. (2007). *The art of power*. Harper One.

7 Ryan, R. M., Donald, J. N., & Bradshaw, E. L. (2021). Mindfulness and motivation: A process view using self-determination theory. *Current Directions in Psychological Science*, *30*(4), 300–306.

8 Deci, E. L., Ryan, R. M., Schultz, P. P., & Niemiec, C. P. (2015). Being aware and functioning fully: Mindfulness and interest taking within self-determination theory. In K. W. Brown, J. D. Creswel, & R. M. Ryan (Eds.), *Handbook of mindfulness: Theory, research, and practice* (pp. 112–129). The Guilford Press.

9 Schultz, P. P., & Ryan, R. M. (2015). The "why," "what," and "how" of healthy self-regulation: Mindfulness and well-being from a self-determination theory perspective. In B. D. Ostafin, M . D. Robinson, & B. P. Meier (Eds.), *Handbook of mindfulness and self-regulation* (pp. 81–94). Springer New York, NY.

10 Ryan, R. M., Donald, J. N., & Bradshaw, E. L. (2021). Mindfulness and motivation: A process view using self-determination theory. *Current Directions in Psychological Science*, *30*(4), 300–306.

Cultivate Upward Spirals

1 Fredrickson, B. L., & Joiner, T. (2018). Reflections on positive emotions and upward spirals. *Perspectives on Psychological Science*, *13*(2), 194–199.

2 Alexander, R., Aragón, O. R., Bookwala, J., Cherbuin, N., Gatt, J. M., Kahrilas, I. J., Kästner, N., Lawrence, A., Lowe, L., Morrison, R. G., Mueller, S. C., Nusslock, R., Papadelis, C., Polnaszek, K. L., Helene Richter, S., Silton, R. L., & Styliadis, C. (2021). The neuroscience of positive emotions and affect: Implications for cultivating happiness and wellbeing. *Neuroscience and Biobehavioral Reviews, 121,* 220–249.

3 Silton, R. L., Kahrilas, I. J., Skymba, H. V., Smith, J., Bryant, F. B., & Heller, W. (2020). Regulating positive emotions: Implications for promoting well-being in individuals with depression. *Emotion, 20*(1), 93–97.

4 Garland, E. L., Fredrickson, B., Kring, A. M., Johnson, D. P., Meyer, P. S., & Penn, D. L. (2010). Upward spirals of positive emotions counter downward spirals of negativity: Insights from the broaden-and-build theory and affective neuroscience on the treatment of emotion dysfunctions and deficits in psychopathology. *Clinical Psychology Review, 30*(7), 849–864.

5 Zhun, G. O. N. G., Schooler, J. W., Yong, W. A. N. G., & Mingda, T. A. O. (2018). Research on the relationship between positive emotions, psychological capital and job burnout in enterprises' employees: Based on the broaden-and-build theory of positive emotions. *Canadian Social Science, 14*(5), 42–48.

6 Jackson-Koku, G., & Grime, P. (2019). Emotion regulation and burnout in doctors: A systematic review. *Occupational Medicine, 69*(1), 9–21.

7 Kariou, A., Koutsimani, P., Montgomery, A., & Lainidi, O. (2021). Emotional labor and burnout among teachers: A systematic review. *International Journal of Environmental Research and Public Health, 18*(23), 12760.

8 Zhao, J.-L., Li, X.-H., & Shields, J. (2019). Managing job burnout: The effects of emotion-regulation ability, emotional labor, and positive and negative affect at work. *International Journal of Stress Management, 26*(3), 315–320.

9 Burr, J., & Beck Dallaghan, G. L. (2019). The relationship of emotions and burnout to medical students' academic performance. *Teaching and Learning in Medicine, 31*(5), 479–486.

10 Guan, B., & Jepsen, D. M. (2020). Burnout from emotion regulation at work: The moderating role of gratitude. *Personality and Individual Differences, 156,* 109703.

11 Hanson, R. (2017). Positive neuroplasticity: The neuroscience of mindfulness. In J. Loizzo, M. Neale, & E. J. Wolf (Eds.), *Advances in contemplative psychotherapy: Accelerating healing and transformation* (pp. 48–60). Routledge.

12 Shaffer, J. (2016). Neuroplasticity and clinical practice: Building brain power for health. *Frontiers in Psychology, 7,* 1118.

13 Lardone, A., Liparoti, M., Sorrentino, P., Rucco, R., Jacini, F., Polverino, A., Minino, R., Pesoli, M., Baselice, F., Sorriso, A., Ferraioli, G., Sorrentino, G., & Mandolesi, L. (2018). Mindfulness meditation is related to long-lasting changes in hippocampal functional topology during resting state: A magnetoencephalography study. *Neural Plasticity, 2018.*

14 Hanson, R. (2017). Positive neuroplasticity: The neuroscience of mindfulness. In J. Loizzo, M. Neale, & E. J. Wolf (Eds.), *Advances in contemplative psychotherapy: Accelerating healing and transformation* (pp. 48–60). Routledge.

15 Fuchs, E., & Flügge, G. (2014). Adult neuroplasticity: More than 40 years of research. *Neural Plasticity, 2014.*

16 Sasmita, A. O., Kuruvilla, J., & Ling, A. P. K. (2018). Harnessing neuroplasticity: Modern approaches and clinical future. *International Journal of Neuroscience, 128*(11), 1061–1077.

17 Lardone, A., Liparoti, M., Sorrentino, P., Rucco, R., Jacini, F., Polverino, A., Minino, R., Pesoli, M., Baselice, F., Sorriso, A., Ferraioli, G., Sorrentino, G., & Mandolesi, L. (2018). Mindfulness meditation is related to long-lasting changes in hippocampal functional topology during resting state: A magnetoencephalography study. *Neural Plasticity, 2018.*

18 Luders, E. (2014). Exploring age-related brain degeneration in meditation practitioners. *Annals of the New York Academy of Sciences, 1307*(1), 82–88.

19 Newberg, A. B., Serruya, M., Wintering, N., Moss, A. S., Reibel, D., & Monti, D. A. (2014). Meditation and neurodegenerative diseases. *Annals of the New York Academy of Sciences, 1307*(1), 112–123.

20 Khalsa, D. S. (2015). Stress, meditation, and Alzheimer's disease prevention: Where the evidence stands. *Journal of Alzheimer's Disease, 48*(1), 1–12.

21 Chiesa, A., Calati, R., & Serretti, A. (2011). Does mindfulness training improve cognitive abilities? A systematic review of neuropsychological findings. *Clinical Psychology Review, 31*(3), 449–464.

22 Vago, D. R. (2022). How meditation changes the brain: A neurophilosophical and pragmatic account. In R. Repetti (Ed.), *Routledge handbook on the philosophy of meditation* (pp. 174–191). Routledge.

23 Lutz, A., Slagter, H. A., Dunne, J. D., & Davidson, R. J. (2008). Attention regulation and monitoring in meditation. *Trends in Cognitive Sciences, 12*(4), 163–169.

24 Tang, R., Friston, K. J., & Tang, Y.-Y. (2020). Brief mindfulness meditation induces gray matter changes in a brain hub. *Neural Plasticity, 2020*.

25 Jha, A. P., Denkova, E., Zanesco, A. P., Witkin, J. E., Rooks, J., & Rogers, S. L. (2019). Does mindfulness training help working memory 'work' better? *Current Opinion in Psychology, 28*, 273–278.

26 Hölzel, B. K., Carmody, J., Vangel, M., Congleton, C., Yerramsetti, S. M., Gard, T., & Lazar, S. W. (2011). Mindfulness practice leads to increases in regional brain gray matter density. Psychiatry Research, *191*(1), 36-43.

27 Sharma, Y., & Agarwal, T. (2020, February). Functional brain mapping of meditation using fMRI. *Proceedings of International Conference on Drug Discovery (ICDD)*.

28 Bossert, L., Arzberger, K., Dorok, F., Kern, J., Stickler, C.,

Wunderlich, M., & Tran, U. S. (2023). The effects of mindfulness-based interventions on telomere length and telomerase activity: A systematic review and meta-analysis. *Mindfulness, 14*(3), 495–509.

ACKNOWLEDGMENTS

Writing a book like this represents a long and arduous journey. There were many individuals who generously gave their time and support, and I am deeply appreciative of them all.

Carol Kauffman, mentor and dear friend, has been a key presence on my healing and writing journey, helping me to move beyond pain and fear and to reclaim my voice as an author, a coach, and a healer.

I am deeply grateful to the many physician readers who took the time to review multiple iterations of the book and provide helpful feedback. I am particularly grateful to Sue Tobert, Avani Prabhakar, Les Schwab, Brett Levine, Susie O'Horo, Jane Liebschutz, and Wendy Pentland. A big thank you to the members of the Peekskill Writing Table for their expert critiques.

A particular thanks to Beatrice Stipek and Liz Drance, patient and expert readers of early drafts who provided key insights that shaped the future direction of the manuscript.

My understanding of mindfulness has been shaped by many individuals who have made discovery in human psychology and mindfulness their life's work. Tara Brach and Jack Kornfield have been two key guides, among many others. Thich Nhat Hanh, Pema Chodron, Jon Kabat-Zinn, Sharon Salzberg, Joseph Goldstein, and the Dalai Lama have been particularly impactful in my mindfulness journey.

I am forever indebted to the physicians I have had the privilege of coaching over the past decade. These physicians came to coaching struggling with burnout, loss of purpose, and exhaustion. Each demonstrated their tremendous commitment to excellence in patient care and stepped out of the patterns learned in training to share their vulnerability with deep honesty and integrity. I greatly appreciate their trust in me as their coach, and the opportunity to assist each and every one in becoming *Mindful MDs*.

I also want to acknowledge the many patients and families who allowed me to participate in their sacred end-of-life journeys, providing deep learning about impermanence and suffering, and the importance of compassion, connection, and true autonomy.

I have tremendous gratitude and appreciation for my younger selves, who lived through much trauma and had the grit, creativity, resilience, and goodness to prevail.

A very big thanks to Sheila Parr for her wonderful cover design and to Maggie Billard for her meticulousness in proofreading and indexing.

My thanks, as well, to Margaret Moore and others at the Harvard Institute of Coaching for their wonderful collegiality and their commitment to the field of physician coaching.

My deepest gratitude goes to my son, Daavi Gazelle, who worked tirelessly editing many iterations of this book. A gifted writer himself (author at age 23 of the mindful college admissions guide, *The Kids Who Get In*), he is also an astute and dedicated mindfulness practitioner. Daavi was extraordinarily insightful and patient in providing his assistance. I am forever grateful that he is the beautiful and ever-growing man who I am very fortunate to have as my son.

A deep bow of appreciation to all the physicians who have joined the *Mindful MD* movement, including those in the private physician Facebook group of that name.

If you want more support reclaiming joy and fulfillment in the career you've worked so hard for, learn more about coaching and download free resources at www.gailgazelle.com.

AUTHOR BIOGRAPHIES

Dr. Gail Gazelle is a globally recognized leader in physician burnout and coaching. She is a part-time Assistant Professor of Medicine at Harvard Medical School and an International Coach Federation Master Certified Coach for physicians and physician leaders. Dr. Gazelle began her career as an internist and hospice physician and then pivoted to become a physician coach. Over the past decade, she has coached over 500 physician leaders and physicians.

Dr. Gazelle is the author of *Everyday Resilience. A Practical Guide to Build Inner Strength and Weather Life's Challenges* (2020) and the Harvard Health Guide *Mindfulness Support for Alzheimer's Caregivers* (2013). She combines cutting-edge research in neuroscience, emotional intelligence, and mindfulness with evidence-based coaching approaches, providing the widest possible strategies to help clients advance their leadership and leave burnout behind.

A certified mindfulness teacher, Dr. Gazelle is a dynamic and engaging speaker, providing keynotes, workshops, and retreats across the globe. Her articles have been published in such journals as the *New England Journal of Medicine*, the *Journal of the American Geriatrics Society*, and the *Journal of General Internal Medicine*.

When not working, Dr. Gazelle can be found outdoors walking with her canine pals or dabbling in watercolors and fabric collage.

Find out more at www.gailgazelle.com.

Daavi Gazelle is an entrepreneur and mindfulness junkie. He attended Vanderbilt University, majoring in Human and Organizational Development, and Mathematics. Prior to that, he spent a year working in Boston public schools as a City Year Americorps member. Daavi has completed three Vipassana silent retreats and has been practicing mindfulness meditation since 2015.

Daavi is the author of *The Kids Who Get In (2020)*, a mindfulness guide to authentic college admissions. Daavi has worked in the family coaching practice in different capacities since 2017 and is now the Director of Client Success and Chief Growth Officer, where he focuses on making sure that the physicians we serve get the most from their coaching experience.

When not working, Daavi is an avid traveler and loves all things basketball.

INDEX

CPSIA information can be obtained
at www.ICGtesting.com
Printed in the USA
BVHW050004280623
666449BV00016B/869

9 780979 817601